Trying to Conceive Through Faith

• Journal •

A Daily Guide for TTCTF

How Being Consistent in Pursuing God
Allowed Us to Conceive

Lillian Day

www.TTCTF.com

Trying to Conceive Through Faith Journal

First Edition

ISBN: 978-1-7320564-0-4

www.TTCTF.com

A special thanks to God for guiding me on this journey and allowing me to share it with anyone who needs it. Also, thank you so much, Thomas, for your continued support and to Kitty for your encouragement. I am so blessed and so grateful that no words can fully express my gratitude and joy! - Lillian Day

Edited by Daphne Parsekian

Book cover designed by Abhishek A. Naik (Makak Studios)

Biblical References

TABLE OF CONTENTS

EXTRAS

GETTING STARTED

This is your 91-day journal that includes a bonus of 10 additional days. It is designed to work alongside the *Trying To Conceive Through Faith (TTCTF)* book. This journal is to be used for self-reflection, encouragement, focusing on scripture and ultimately, to draw closer to God.

Each week focuses on one of the chapters from the *TTCTF* book.

As you work through the journal, pray for revelation, understanding, and wisdom. Pray for God's guidance so you grow each day in faith, hope, and understanding of God's will for your life.

Each Day Has the Following:

- A quick overview to prayerfully consider
- A Bible verse
- Two beginning statements to complete
- Four questions to answer
- A checklist for the day
- An area for your notes

There is no wrong way to fill out this journal. Below are some examples of how you can use it.

Drawing Areas

Some questions encourage you to draw. For example, you will be asked to draw the size of your faith. Use this space to be creative as you are thinking about the question.

Daily Gratitude

Each day has a gratitude section. It is important to spend a couple of minutes a day finding something to be grateful for. Please write down personal gratitudes, not general things. The more personal, the better as it reminds us how blessed we are by God and how faithful he is to us.

Join Us

Be sure to join the Through Faith community at ttctf.com

Terminology

- **2WW -** Two-Week Wait
- **AF -** Aunt Flo (menstrual cycle)
- **BBT -** Basal Body Temperature
- **BD -** Baby Dance (Intercourse)
- **BFN -** Big Fat Negative
- **BFP -** Big Fat Positive
- **CD -** Cycle Day
- **CM -** Cervical Mucus
- **DH -** Dear Husband
- **DPO -** Days Past Ovulation
- **EWCM -** Egg-White Cervical Mucus
- **HPT -** Home Pregnancy Test
- **O or OV -** Ovulation
- **OPK -** Ovulation Predictor Kit
- **TTC -** Trying to Conceive
- **TTCTF -** Trying to Conceive Through Faith

I pray in the name of Jesus that this journal would encourage you to draw closer to God and help your faith grow as you are TTCTF.

WEEK 1

RENEWED HOPE

GOAL

To make your past "history" so you can focus on the promises of God and his goodness!

DAILY PRAYER

God, you know how badly I want a baby. My soul is aching, and my body feels incomplete. My life feels incomplete. My hope is dried out, my heart is throbbing, and this emptiness is echoing into every area of my life.

I have been trying to make my body do what you designed it to do, and I have come up empty. I feel like I have failed; my body has failed.

I now see the hope I have had and the plans I have made require more of you.

I will no longer put my hope, my faith, and my trust in this body; they are now completely in you. You are the God who parted the Red Sea for safe passage. You closed the mouth of the lions for Daniel. You are the God who made Shadrach, Meshach, and Abednego untouchable in the fiery furnace. You are the God who delivered food in the desert. You, God, have made water flow from a stone. You have made blind men see. You have raised men from the grave. You continually show us life where there is death. You, oh God, are the God of miracles, and you are certainly the God who opens the womb of the barren woman.

There is nothing outside of your reach; there is nothing you cannot make whole. Every mountain I face is nothing compared to your greatness.

Please forgive me for my frustration and emptiness.

Please remove this brokenness.

Please let me be filled with your love and peace.

Please show me how to grow my faith.

I believe, God, that you hear my prayers, and I know without a doubt you are capable of answering them. Today I ask you to reveal why you have not answered this prayer.

I know your love for me is so great that no matter how many times I fail, you are there to pick me up. You are the God of love and of mercy, and I need them both.

I will no longer try to conceive without faith; my faith is in you. Today is a new start, a new beginning that you have given me. I will seek you for answers and wait for your direction.

Today my faith and hope are restored in you.

Thank you, God, for your faithfulness!

In Jesus' name,
Amen

Date: / /

Day 1: Hope Worth Having

Hoping is the first step in growing our faith in God. Hope means we may not know what the plan is but we believe it is possible. If we hope in God while TTCTF, we will always have something to hope for, even on our worst days.

SCRIPTURE

Psalm 42:11, "Why are you cast down, O my soul, and why are you in turmoil within me? Hope in God; for I shall again praise him, my salvation and my God."

MARK WHERE YOU ARE TODAY

Heartache 0% ______ 100%

Hope 0% ______ 100%

Determination 0% ______ 100%

Today I am grateful for:

___

___

___

___

Today my hope is in:

___

___

___

___

What habits are negatively affecting your hope?

___

___

___

___

How can you renew your hope today?

___

___

___

___

___

WRITE YOUR TTC STORY UP UNTIL NOW:

Date: / /

Day 2: Find Genuine Happiness

It gets easy to put a mask on in front of other people and pretend to be happy when we feel like we are dying inside. That mask is there to protect us, but we have to take it off from time to time. We cannot keep pretending to be happy if we are not. Instead, we should face our hurt and pain and search God for genuine happiness.

SCRIPTURE

2 Corinthians 12:10, "For the sake of Christ, then, I am content with weaknesses, insults, hardships, persecutions, and calamities. For when I am weak, then I am strong."

MARK WHERE YOU ARE TODAY

Anger	0%		100%
Resentment	0%		100%
Happiness	0%		100%

Today I am grateful for:

____

____

____

____

Today I can be happy because:

____

____

____

____

What can you do today to trust God with your pain?

____

____

____

____

Is it possible for you to be happy while you are TTCTF?

____

____

____

____

____

WHAT HAS ROBBED YOU FROM BEING HAPPY?

TODAY'S CHECKLIST

- ▢ Read the Bible
- ▢ Pray
- ▢ Read TTCTF
- ▢ TTCTF Journal
- ▢ ____________
- ▢ ____________
- ▢ ____________
- ▢ ____________
- ▢ ____________
- ▢ ____________
- ▢ ____________

NOTES

Date: / /

Day 3: Focusing on God Instead of the Signs

Hope and excitement while TTC may turn into anxiety, depression, and hopelessness. If the two-week wait every month has us obsessed over the signs of pregnancy, we will not have peace. Somehow, there is always a sign, either smells, breast sensitivity, or whatever it is, to try to predict pregnancy. Unfortunately, we will not know before that two-week wait is over. We need to forget about the signs and focus on God.

SCRIPTURE

Psalm 37:7, “Be still before the LORD and wait patiently for him; fret not yourself over the one who prospers in his way, over the man who carries out evil devices!”

MARK WHERE YOU ARE TODAY

Anxiety 0% ______ 100%

Depression 0% ______ 100%

Peace 0% ______ 100%

Today I am grateful for:

____

____

____

____

Today I will stop looking for these signs:

____

____

____

How does reading into signs take away from our hope?

____

____

____

____

Why is taking an early pregnancy test a bad idea?

____

____

____

____

WHAT CAN YOU DO TO HONOR GOD WHILE YOU WAIT?

TODAY'S CHECKLIST

- ☐ Read the Bible
- ☐ Pray
- ☐ Read TTCTF
- ☐ TTCTF Journal
- ☐ ____________
- ☐ ____________
- ☐ ____________
- ☐ ____________
- ☐ ____________
- ☐ ____________
- ☐ ____________

NOTES

Date: / /

Day 4: Seeking God

In the midst of the waiting, the frustration and pain may cause us to lose sight of God. It becomes easy to forget that he has the answers. If we search for God, he will provide direction and purpose for us. We have to actively search him no matter what our circumstances are.

SCRIPTURE

Acts 17:27, "so that they should seek God, in the hope that they might feel their way toward him and find him. Yet he is actually not far from each one of us..."

MARK WHERE YOU ARE TODAY

Frustration 0% ______ 100%

Pain 0% ______ 100%

Faith 0% ______ 100%

Today I am grateful for:

Today I will have faith because:

Where do you see God working in your life?

How can you let go of your frustration and pain while TTCTF?

WHAT CAN YOU DO TO SEEK GOD?

TODAY'S CHECKLIST

- ▢ Read the Bible
- ▢ Pray
- ▢ Read TTCTF
- ▢ TTCTF Journal
- ▢ ______
- ▢ ______
- ▢ ______
- ▢ ______
- ▢ ______
- ▢ ______
- ▢ ______

NOTES

Date: / /

Day 5: Delighting in the Lord

When we know God can answer our prayers yet still have an empty womb, we have to make sure we are not angry with God. If we blame God for our circumstances, it will only distance us from the answers and direction he has for us. If we delight in God, even in our pain, we are keeping that communication open and allowing God to direct us.

SCRIPTURE

Psalm 145:16-18, "You open your hand; you satisfy the desire of every living thing. The LORD is righteous in all his ways and kind in all his works. The LORD is near to all who call on him, to all who call on him in truth."

MARK WHERE YOU ARE TODAY

Brokenness	0%	______	100%
Anger	0%	______	100%
Joy	0%	______	100%

Today I am grateful for:

______

______

______

______

Today I have joy because:

______

______

______

______

How does the kindness of the Lord give you hope?

______

______

______

______

How do you let go of hurt and replace it with faith?

______

______

______

______

______

HOW DO YOU DELIGHT IN THE LORD WHILE TTCTF?

TODAY'S CHECKLIST

- ▢ Read the Bible
- ▢ Pray
- ▢ Read TTCTF
- ▢ TTCTF Journal
- ▢ ______________
- ▢ ______________
- ▢ ______________
- ▢ ______________
- ▢ ______________
- ▢ ______________
- ▢ ______________

NOTES

Date: / /

Day 6: Seeking Revelation

God gives revelation through prayer, through wisdom from others, and through his Word. Without revelation, we have blind spots. We do not have a complete understanding of what God wants from us. We need to prayerfully seek revelation about our sin and turn it into obedience to the Word so we honor him with our life and are not deceived by our sin.

SCRIPTURE

Ephesians 1:7–8, "In him we have redemption through his blood, the forgiveness of our trespasses, according to the riches of his grace, which he lavished upon us, in all wisdom and insight..."

MARK WHERE YOU ARE TODAY

Wisdom 0% ______ 100%

Discernment 0% ______ 100%

Patience 0% ______ 100%

Today I am grateful for:

______

______

______

______

Today I pray for revelation for:

______

______

______

______

How have your emotions clouded the perspective God wants to share?

______

______

______

______

When revelation reveals sin, how do we find redemption?

______

______

______

______

______

HOW CAN YOU BENEFIT FROM GOD'S REVELATION?

TODAY'S CHECKLIST

- ▢ Read the Bible
- ▢ Pray
- ▢ Read TTCTF
- ▢ TTCTF Journal
- ▢ ____
- ▢ ____
- ▢ ____
- ▢ ____
- ▢ ____
- ▢ ____
- ▢ ____

NOTES

Date: / /

Day 7: Following God in Faith

God is waiting for us to reach out in faith and follow him. If we seek God, we will find him. If we find him, he will reveal, guide, and direct our paths. But this is our choice. This is our commitment. We have to take action. We have to pick up the Bible, read it and pray each day. We have to choose to prioritize faith.

SCRIPTURE	*Today I am grateful for:*
Jeremiah 29:13-14, "You will seek me and find me, when you seek me with all your heart. I will be found by you, declares the LORD..."	

What is standing in the way of you fully committing to God?

How can following God help you conceive?

Write your commitment statement to God below while you are TTCTF.

WHAT DOES TTCTF MEAN TO YOU?

TODAY'S CHECKLIST

- ▢ Read the Bible
- ▢ Pray
- ▢ Read TTCTF
- ▢ TTCTF Journal
- ▢ ____________
- ▢ ____________
- ▢ ____________
- ▢ ____________
- ▢ ____________
- ▢ ____________
- ▢ ____________

NOTES

WEEK 2

CONQUERING FEAR

GOAL

To identify fears that affect our relationship with God so we can overcome and replace them with faith.

DAILY PRAYER

God, I thank you for your love and your protection over my life. I have been broken for too long and see that I need to give you back control.

Please search my heart and reveal areas I need to work on.

Please give me the spirit of wisdom and discernment to better understand the sin in my life so I can honor you.

I know fear is controlling and can distort my relationship with you. I do not want to give the devil a foothold anymore.

Please forgive me, Lord, for dishonoring you with my fears and my anger about not having children yet. I know you are bigger than any obstacle, and I realize that as my faith grows, so will my relationship with you.

I pray specifically about having children.

I know it does not matter what a doctor says or how long we have been trying. My faith is not in my doctors or in my past; my faith is in you alone. Since you created the heavens, the earth, and the process of procreation, I know and believe in my heart that through faith, you will hear and answer my prayers with a healthy, happy baby.

Today is a new beginning, and I am grateful you have started me on this journey of faith.

I give you all the honor and praise.

In Jesus' name,
Amen

Date: / /

Day 8: Identify Fears

Having children means being responsible for another human being. This responsibility lasts a lifetime, and with so much pressure, it is possible for fear to slip in. We need to identify those fears so they do not become a stumbling block to our faith.

SCRIPTURE

2 Timothy 1:7, "for God gave us a spirit not of fear but of power and love and self-control."

FEAR VERSUS FAITH

Color the pie chart with your percentage of fear. The remaining represents your faith.

Today I am grateful for:

Today I trust God with:

What fears do you have about pregnancy, delivery, and parenthood?

How can you eliminate your fears?

HOW DOES FEAR AFFECT YOUR FAITH?

TODAY'S CHECKLIST

- ▢ Read the Bible
- ▢ Pray
- ▢ Read TTCTF
- ▢ TTCTF Journal
- ▢
- ▢
- ▢
- ▢
- ▢
- ▢
- ▢

NOTES

Date: / /

Day 9: Strong and Courageous

As believers, we are called to be strong and courageous and not to be fearful. We can only do so if we recognize that we have God with us. We are never alone; we have the full protection of our God who loves and cares for us. Our fears only have strength if we feel like we are alone, without God. Thankfully he is with us wherever we go.

SCRIPTURE

Joshua 1:9, “Have I not commanded you? Be strong and courageous. Do not be frightened, and do not be dismayed, for the LORD your God is with you wherever you go.”

FEAR VERSUS FAITH

Color the pie chart with your percentage of fear. The remaining represents your faith.

Today I am grateful for:

Today I will be courageous about:

How can you be strong while TTCTF?

How can you be courageous while TTCTF?

HOW DOES GOD'S PRESENCE HELP COMBAT YOUR FEARS?

TODAY'S CHECKLIST

- ▢ Read the Bible
- ▢ Pray
- ▢ Read TTCTF
- ▢ TTCTF Journal
- ▢ ____________
- ▢ ____________
- ▢ ____________
- ▢ ____________
- ▢ ____________
- ▢ ____________
- ▢ ____________

NOTES

Date: / /

Day 10: Finding the Right Focus

If we are focused on God and understand who he is, our fears will not have enough substance to be scary. If we focus on our fears instead of God, we will forget the strength and power that he has, and our fears will appear bigger than God, making them seem legitimate.

SCRIPTURE

Philippians 4:8, "Finally, brothers, whatever is true, whatever is honorable, whatever is just, whatever is pure, whatever is lovely, whatever is commendable, if there is any excellence, if there is anything worthy of praise, think about these things."

FEAR VERSUS FAITH

Color the pie chart with your percentage of fear. The remaining represents your faith.

Today I am grateful for:

Today I will focus on:

What are the repercussions of living in fear?

What can you focus on when your fears come up?

LIST WHAT IS TRUE, HONORABLE, JUST, PURE, LOVELY, COMMENDABLE, OR WORTHY OF PRAISE TODAY:

TODAY'S CHECKLIST

- ▢ Read the Bible
- ▢ Pray
- ▢ Read TTCTF
- ▢ TTCTF Journal
- ▢
- ▢
- ▢
- ▢
- ▢
- ▢
- ▢

NOTES

Date: / /

Day 11: Eliminating Manipulation by Addressing Fears

The enemy uses anything he can to separate us from God. He is a divider and does not want us to be blessed with a baby. Our fears can be used to manipulate us from trusting God. If we recognize this manipulation, we can overcome it.

SCRIPTURE

2 Corinthians 11:14, "And no wonder, for even Satan disguises himself as an angel of light."

FEAR VERSUS FAITH

Color the pie chart with your percentage of fear. The remaining represents your faith.

Today I am grateful for:

Today I will not let the enemy:

How have you been manipulated by the enemy?

What are 3 reasons the enemy does not want you to conceive?

HOW DOES FEAR SEPARATE YOU FROM GOD'S PLAN?

TODAY'S CHECKLIST

- ▢ Read the Bible
- ▢ Pray
- ▢ Read TTCTF
- ▢ TTCTF Journal
- ▢ ____________
- ▢ ____________
- ▢ ____________
- ▢ ____________
- ▢ ____________
- ▢ ____________
- ▢ ____________

NOTES

Date: / /

Day 12: Trusting God With Fears

Fear is often rationalized and justified. The justifications we make are lies that stop us from trusting God and keep us prisoners to our fears. With God, we do not have to be afraid, because he is bigger than our greatest fear. Whatever justification we have, it is not worth missing out on conceiving our child. It is time to trust God with the things we fear.

SCRIPTURE

John 14:27, "Peace I leave with you; my peace I give you. I do not give to you as the world gives. Do not let your hearts be troubled and do not be afraid."

FEAR VERSUS FAITH

Color the pie chart with your percentage of fear. The remaining represents your faith.

Today I am grateful for:

Today I will trust God because:

How does fear override God's authority in your life?

Why is peace a good trait to pray for while TTCTF?

HOW CAN YOU HAVE PEACE ABOUT PREGNANCY AND PARENTHOOD?

TODAY'S CHECKLIST

- ▢ Read the Bible
- ▢ Pray
- ▢ Read TTCTF
- ▢ TTCTF Journal
- ▢ ____________
- ▢ ____________
- ▢ ____________
- ▢ ____________
- ▢ ____________
- ▢ ____________
- ▢ ____________

NOTES

Date: / /

Day 13: Defining the Origin of Fear

Fear has a reason for existing. The conscious and subconscious mind include fear as a form of protection. We have to find the origin of our fears to reconcile them so we can eliminate the power they have over us.

SCRIPTURE

2 Corinthians 5:17, "Therefore, if anyone is in Christ, he is a new creation. The old has passed away; behold, the new has come."

FEAR VERSUS FAITH

Color the pie chart with your percentage of fear. The remaining represents your faith.

Today I am grateful for:

Today I can renew my perspective because:

How did your fears originate?

How can you move past the origin of your fears to replace them with faith?

LIST THE WAYS GOD HAS RENEWED YOU AS A NEW CREATION IN CHRIST:

TODAY'S CHECKLIST

- ☐ Read the Bible
- ☐ Pray
- ☐ Read TTCTF
- ☐ TTCTF Journal
- ☐ ____________
- ☐ ____________
- ☐ ____________
- ☐ ____________
- ☐ ____________
- ☐ ____________
- ☐ ____________

NOTES

Date: / /

Day 14: Relying on God for Strength

When we rely on God in our weaknesses, then all we have are strengths. When we serve God, who sees what is coming, we can trust that any obstacle we face will be for a purpose. He will help us to grow and overcome so that purpose can be fulfilled. Relying on God is like strength training; it requires us to continuously convert our fears to faith.

SCRIPTURE

1 Chronicles 16:11, "Seek the LORD and his strength; seek his presence continually!"

FEAR VERSUS FAITH

Color the pie chart with your percentage of fear. The remaining represents your faith.

Today I am grateful for:

Today I will get my strength from:

What has God's strength helped you through in the past?

When do you rely on yourself instead of God?

HOW HAVE YOU ELIMINATED FEAR REGARDING PREGNANCY, DELIVERY, AND PARENTHOOD?

TODAY'S CHECKLIST

- ▢ Read the Bible
- ▢ Pray
- ▢ Read TTCTF
- ▢ TTCTF Journal
- ▢ __________
- ▢ __________
- ▢ __________
- ▢ __________
- ▢ __________
- ▢ __________
- ▢ __________

NOTES

WEEK 3

WAITING

GOAL

To ensure you are not the reason God is waiting to bless you, by actively pursuing Him.

DAILY PRAYER

God, I have been deceived in the time I have spent waiting. I know my patience has been tested and run out. Now I am faced with the question "Have I done enough?" Have I taken this time to search you, to draw near to you, and to be committed to you no matter what your answer to my prayer is? I am so sad to say I have not. I have failed in my commitment to you.

I have been frozen, waiting for an answer, and I do not believe this is what you want from me. I know you want a personal relationship with me. You want me in your Word and praying to you daily. You want me to seek you in the good times and the bad times. This time has been a trial, and I need your help. I need more of you.

If this time of waiting shows me one thing, please let it be that you are the answer to everything I need. Not time or science. Just you, God.

I will no longer wait and do nothing. I will use this time to draw near to you. I believe if I am in your Word, I will understand you more. I will hear more from you, and I will know how to be in your will so you can answer this prayer of pregnancy.

No one in the world knows me like you do, God. Please help me to make my ways your ways; help me search for you more than I have for this pregnancy.

Please show me what to do as I wait for you to answer this prayer so you do not have to wait to bless me any longer.

I love you, Lord!

In Jesus' name,
Amen

Date: / /

Day 15: Active Waiting

God answers prayers. If he is not answering our prayers, there is a reason for it. We need to take responsibility by ensuring our lives line up with what God expects from us. Thankfully, God shows us mercy but we have to put the effort in. We cannot continue to be idle while we wait.

SCRIPTURE

Isaiah 30:18, "Therefore the LORD waits to be gracious to you, and therefore he exalts himself to show mercy to you. For the LORD is a God of justice; blessed are all those who wait for him."

RATE YOUR EFFORT TODAY

Praying	0%		100%
Reading the Bible	0%		100%
Listening for God	0%		100%

Today I am grateful for:

Today I think God is waiting for:

How have you spent your time waiting?

Why is God waiting while you are TTCTF?

WHAT CAN YOU DO DIFFERENTLY AS YOU WAIT TO CONCEIVE?

TODAY'S CHECKLIST

- ▢ Read the Bible
- ▢ Pray
- ▢ Read TTCTF
- ▢ TTCTF Journal
- ▢ ____________
- ▢ ____________
- ▢ ____________
- ▢ ____________
- ▢ ____________
- ▢ ____________
- ▢ ____________

NOTES

Date: / /

Day 16: Perfect Timing

God has perfect timing. He has the foresight to know what is coming next, which makes his timing intentional. Our timing only focuses on guessing what the future holds. When we trust God while TTCTF, we can have peace, hope, and faith that God's timing is better than our own.

SCRIPTURE

Ecclesiastes 3:1, "For everything there is a season, and a time for every matter under heaven..."

RATE YOUR EFFORT TODAY

Praying 0% ______ 100%

Reading the Bible 0% ______ 100%

Listening for God 0% ______ 100%

Today I am grateful for:

Today I think God is waiting for:

What do you think is the purpose of waiting while you are TTCTF?

How can you trust God with his timing while you are TTCTF?

WHAT TRIGGERS YOU TO LOSE PATIENCE WHILE YOU ARE WAITING?

TODAY'S CHECKLIST

- ▢ Read the Bible
- ▢ Pray
- ▢ Read TTCTF
- ▢ TTCTF Journal
- ▢ ____________
- ▢ ____________
- ▢ ____________
- ▢ ____________
- ▢ ____________
- ▢ ____________
- ▢ ____________

NOTES

Date: / /

Day 17: Peace While Waiting

When we completely accept that God is our loving, caring Father, then we can have peace while we wait. We can learn more about him each day through reading the Word and through prayer. God wants us to know him, honor him, and be able to receive his blessings. He wants us to have peace while we are TTCTF.

SCRIPTURE

James 4:8, "Draw near to God, and he will draw near to you."

RATE YOUR EFFORT TODAY

Praying	0%		100%
Reading the Bible	0%		100%
Listening for God	0%		100%

Today I am grateful for:

Today I think God is waiting for:

What in your life separates you from God?

When you do not have peace, how do you feel?

HOW WOULD DRAWING NEAR TO GOD GIVE YOU PEACE?

TODAY'S CHECKLIST

- ▢ Read the Bible
- ▢ Pray
- ▢ Read TTCTF
- ▢ TTCTF Journal
- ▢ ____________
- ▢ ____________
- ▢ ____________
- ▢ ____________
- ▢ ____________
- ▢ ____________
- ▢ ____________

NOTES

Date: / /

Day 18: Guidance While Waiting

If we are expecting God's blessings, we have to serve him according to his Word. The Bible makes it very clear that if we are outside of God's will, we will miss out on blessings. We need to search the Word for guidance, to reveal what areas we need to work on, as we wait to receive this gift.

SCRIPTURE

Deuteronomy 7:9, "Know therefore that the LORD your God is God, the faithful God who keeps covenant and steadfast love with those who love him and keep his commandments, to a thousand generations..."

RATE YOUR EFFORT TODAY

Praying 0% ( ) 100%

Reading the Bible 0% ( ) 100%

Listening for God 0% ( ) 100%

Today I am grateful for:

____

____

____

____

Today I think God is waiting for:

____

____

____

____

How do you show God you love him?

____

____

____

____

____

How can you commit to following God in whatever direction he shows you?

____

____

____

____

____

HOW DOES GOD'S FAITHFULNESS MAKE HIS PLANS TRUSTWORTHY AS YOU ARE TTCTF?

TODAY'S CHECKLIST

- ▢ Read the Bible
- ▢ Pray
- ▢ Read TTCTF
- ▢ TTCTF Journal
- ▢ ____________
- ▢ ____________
- ▢ ____________
- ▢ ____________
- ▢ ____________
- ▢ ____________
- ▢ ____________

NOTES

Date: / /

Day 19: Obedience While Waiting

Obeying God means we need to follow the commands in the Bible. When we obey God, we have access to the blessings found in the Bible. When we do not receive the blessings found in the Bible, it may be due to disobeying God.

SCRIPTURE

Deuteronomy 28:1–2, "And if you faithfully obey the voice of the LORD your God, being careful to do all his commandments that I command you today, the LORD your God will set you high above all the nations of the earth. And all these blessings shall come upon you and overtake you, if you obey the voice of the LORD your God."

RATE YOUR EFFORT TODAY

Praying 0% ______ 100%

Reading the Bible 0% ______ 100%

Listening for God 0% ______ 100%

Today I am grateful for:

____

____

____

____

____

Today I think God is waiting for:

____

____

____

____

____

How are you disobeying God in your life?

____

____

____

____

How does your disobedience affect your relationship with God?

____

____

____

____

LIST 5 COMMANDS IN THE BIBLE THAT YOU STRUGGLE WITH:

TODAY'S CHECKLIST

- ▢ Read the Bible
- ▢ Pray
- ▢ Read TTCTF
- ▢ TTCTF Journal
- ▢ ____________
- ▢ ____________
- ▢ ____________
- ▢ ____________
- ▢ ____________
- ▢ ____________
- ▢ ____________

NOTES

Date: / /

Day 20: Receiving All of the Fruit

When our impatience proves to be unfruitful, we have to try something else. When we serve God the way he wants us to, he is free to give us every blessing promised in the Bible. If we want God's abundance, we have to do whatever the Bible says as we wait for conception.

SCRIPTURE

Ephesians 3:20, "Now to him who is able to do far more abundantly than all that we ask or think, according to the power at work within us..."

RATE YOUR EFFORT TODAY

Praying	0% ____________	100%
Reading the Bible	0% ____________	100%
Listening for God	0% ____________	100%

Today I am grateful for:

____

____

____

____

Today I think God is waiting for:

____

____

____

____

How do you show gratitude for the blessings you have today?

____

____

____

____

____

What are the details of a time when God blessed you?

____

____

____

____

____

WHAT ARE OTHER PROMISES FOUND IN THE BIBLE THAT YOU WANT FOR YOUR LIFE?

TODAY'S CHECKLIST

- ▢ Read the Bible
- ▢ Pray
- ▢ Read TTCTF
- ▢ TTCTF Journal
- ▢ ____
- ▢ ____
- ▢ ____
- ▢ ____
- ▢ ____
- ▢ ____
- ▢ ____

NOTES

Date: / /

Day 21: Fully Committed

If we want to ensure God is not waiting on us to bless us, we need to fully commit to him. We need to carve out time to serve and honor him so we can learn what the Bible says about being fully committed to God. When we put God first, we stop getting in God's way to bless us.

SCRIPTURE

1 Chronicles 16:11, "Seek the LORD and his strength; seek his presence continually!"

RATE YOUR EFFORT TODAY

Praying 0% ( ) 100%

Reading the Bible 0% ( ) 100%

Listening for God 0% ( ) 100%

Today I am grateful for:

Today I think God is waiting for:

How do you feel when God is not giving you the answer you want right now?

What does the Bible say about being lukewarm?

WHAT DO YOU NEED TO SURRENDER TODAY TO FULLY COMMIT TO GOD?

TODAY'S CHECKLIST

- ▢ Read the Bible
- ▢ Pray
- ▢ Read TTCTF
- ▢ TTCTF Journal
- ▢ ______
- ▢ ______
- ▢ ______
- ▢ ______
- ▢ ______
- ▢ ______
- ▢ ______

NOTES

WEEK 4

THROUGH FAITH

GOAL

To take responsibility for trusting God while you are TTCTF, because he has remained faithful even as you lacked faith.

DAILY PRAYER

God, my eyes are fixed on you, and I will no longer let my faith waver. My circumstances do not change you. My sin does not change you. You are the only constant in my life. You are the unmovable Rock. You are the unwavering King and my Holy God.

When my eyes see you for the glorious Father you are, I am certain nothing is impossible. I have let this time cloud my vision of you, and it has taken away my faith. It has made my faith weak and even useless.

Please forgive me for getting caught up in the details and forgetting how great You are. Please continue to renew my hope and strengthen my faith. Please rebuild this brokenness with a restored vision of your greatness.

There has been emptiness in my womb, but you, God, bring life. I will no longer let lack of faith betray the plans you have for me and rob me of your blessings. You take what is broken and make it whole.

Please, God, help me to conceive a baby this next cycle. Please help this baby to be healthy and strong. Please give our baby the best of our traits and pour out an abundance of your peace and joy in his or her life. Please allow this baby to grow to full term. Please bless me with an easy, pain-free delivery and quick recovery.

I rejoice in knowing you have heard this prayer and will answer it because my faith is no longer wavering and my hope and obedience are in you.

Thank you for remaining faithful, even in my unfaithfulness. I love you.

In Jesus' name,
Amen

Date: / /

Day 22: Faith Is the Answer

Faith is one of the most important attributes needed when it comes to seeking a promise from God. Faith does not consider the mountain we are facing; faith looks to God, who can overcome the mountain. Without faith, our doubts make us question God and his abilities.

SCRIPTURE

Hebrews 11:1, "Now faith is the assurance of things hoped for, the conviction of things not seen."

DRAW THE SIZE OF YOUR FAITH

Today I am grateful for:

Today my faith will grow because:

How can faith in God give you assurance and hope?

What makes you focus on the mountain while TTCTF instead of God?

WHAT IS TAKING AWAY FROM YOUR FAITH IN GOD?

TODAY'S CHECKLIST

- ▢ Read the Bible
- ▢ Pray
- ▢ Read TTCTF
- ▢ TTCTF Journal
- ▢ ____________
- ▢ ____________
- ▢ ____________
- ▢ ____________
- ▢ ____________
- ▢ ____________
- ▢ ____________

NOTES

Date: / /

Day 23: Hoping in God

Misplaced hope can be painful when it lets us down over and over again. Thankfully, when we put our hope in God, he delivers. We can have hope in getting pregnant because God has the answers we are seeking!

SCRIPTURE

Isaiah 40:31 (NIV), "but those who hope in the LORD will renew their strength. They will soar on wings like eagles; they will run and not grow weary, they will walk and not be faint."

DRAW THE SIZE OF YOUR FAITH

Today I am grateful for:

Today my faith will grow because:

How has misplaced hope affected your hope in God answering your prayers?

How can you be strengthened if you place your hope in God?

WHAT ARE YOU HOPING FOR WHILE TTCTF?

TODAY'S CHECKLIST

- ▢ Read the Bible
- ▢ Pray
- ▢ Read TTCTF
- ▢ TTCTF Journal
- ▢ ______
- ▢ ______
- ▢ ______
- ▢ ______
- ▢ ______
- ▢ ______
- ▢ ______

NOTES

Date: / /

Day 24: Specificity in Prayers

We need to pray about the details of conception before he or she is conceived. This includes praying for the baby, the pregnancy, and the delivery. We serve a God of details, and if we hope for a boy or a girl, God is the one we can ask for those details. He can handle the desires of our hearts. If we honor him, he will bless us according to his Word.

SCRIPTURE

Mark 11:24, "Therefore I tell you, whatever you ask in prayer, believe that you have received it, and it will be yours."

DRAW THE SIZE OF YOUR FAITH

Today I am grateful for:

Today my faith will grow because:

How can you be more specific in your prayers about TTCTF?

What are you asking God for about your pregnancy and delivery?

WHAT ARE YOU PRAYING FOR ABOUT YOUR BABY?

TODAY'S CHECKLIST

- ▢ Read the Bible
- ▢ Pray
- ▢ Read TTCTF
- ▢ TTCTF Journal
- ▢
- ▢
- ▢
- ▢
- ▢
- ▢
- ▢

NOTES

Date: / /

Day 25: Eliminating Anxiety and Gaining Peace

We either are or are not pregnant. Only time will tell, and being anxious is not what God wants from us. We can replace the anxiety of the unknown by learning more about God, understanding his characteristics, and being filled with his strength and peace.

SCRIPTURE

Philippians 4:6-7, "do not be anxious about anything, but in everything by prayer and supplication with thanksgiving let your requests be made known to God. And the peace of God, which surpasses all understanding, will guard your hearts and your minds in Christ Jesus."

DRAW THE SIZE OF YOUR FAITH

Today I am grateful for:

____

____

____

____

____

Today my faith will grow because:

____

____

____

____

____

How does anxiety steal your peace?

____

____

____

____

What does "the peace of God, which surpasses all understanding" mean to you?

____

____

____

____

WRITE A PRAYER FOR SURRENDERING YOUR ANXIETY AND REQUESTING PEACE:

TODAY'S CHECKLIST

- ▢ Read the Bible
- ▢ Pray
- ▢ Read TTCTF
- ▢ TTCTF Journal
- ▢ ______
- ▢ ______
- ▢ ______
- ▢ ______
- ▢ ______
- ▢ ______
- ▢ ______

NOTES

Date: / /

Day 26: Strength in Trials

When we are not yet pregnant, we have an opportunity to continue in faith or fall apart. Pregnancy, delivery, and parenthood all take strength. We need to find the strength to endure this season to be prepared for the next season.

SCRIPTURE

Proverbs 24:10 (MSG), "If you fall to pieces in a crisis, there wasn't much to you in the first place."

DRAW THE SIZE OF YOUR FAITH

Today I am grateful for:

___

___

___

___

Today my faith will grow because:

___

___

___

___

When is the last time you fell to pieces during your conception journey?

___

___

___

___

What has changed since you last fell apart from the trials of TTC?

___

___

___

___

___

WHAT CAN GIVE YOU STRENGTH AS YOU FACE THIS SEASON OF TTCTF?

TODAY'S CHECKLIST

- ▢ Read the Bible
- ▢ Pray
- ▢ Read TTCTF
- ▢ TTCTF Journal
- ▢ ______________
- ▢ ______________
- ▢ ______________
- ▢ ______________
- ▢ ______________
- ▢ ______________
- ▢ ______________

NOTES

Date: / /

Day 27: Working Toward Useful Faith

If faith apart from works is useless, we need to ensure we are willing to do the work so our faith is useful. We need to actively live by faith through our thoughts, actions, and commitments, which requires diligence.

SCRIPTURE

James 2:20, "Do you want to be shown, you foolish person, that faith apart from works is useless?"

DRAW THE SIZE OF YOUR FAITH

Today I am grateful for:

____

____

____

____

Today my faith will grow because:

____

____

____

____

What have you done that has made your faith useless?

____

____

____

____

____

How is your faith in God an active part of your life?

____

____

____

____

____

WHAT SPECIFIC WORK CAN YOU DO TO SHOW GOD YOUR FAITH IN HIM?

TODAY'S CHECKLIST

- ▢ Read the Bible
- ▢ Pray
- ▢ Read TTCTF
- ▢ TTCTF Journal
- ▢ ____________
- ▢ ____________
- ▢ ____________
- ▢ ____________
- ▢ ____________
- ▢ ____________
- ▢ ____________

NOTES

Date: / /

Day 28: Strengthening Faith

On days when we are broken-hearted, our hurt does not change who God is, but our response can hurt our faith in God. If our circumstances make us doubt, then our faith is being weakened. Instead, we need to lean into God more so we can be strengthened in our weakness.

SCRIPTURE

Psalm 34:18, "The LORD is near to the brokenhearted and saves the crushed in spirit."

DRAW THE SIZE OF YOUR FAITH

Today I am grateful for:

Today my faith will grow because:

What is the hardest part about being consistent in faith?

What makes you question your faith?

HOW DOES KNOWING GOD IS NEAR YOU, WHEN YOU FEEL CRUSHED, HELP YOUR FAITH?

TODAY'S CHECKLIST

- ▢ Read the Bible
- ▢ Pray
- ▢ Read TTCTF
- ▢ TTCTF Journal
- ▢ ____________
- ▢ ____________
- ▢ ____________
- ▢ ____________
- ▢ ____________
- ▢ ____________
- ▢ ____________

NOTES

WEEK 5

GETTING RIGHT WITH GOD

GOAL

To repair any damage in your relationship with God.

DAILY PRAYER

God, please do not let my sin stand in the way of your forgiveness and blessings.

Please show me how to honor you with my whole life, even if it means doing the hard work to get back on track.

I want to follow your will and glorify you. I want our relationship to be completely restored. Please forgive me, God, for everything that is outside of your will.

I ask that you guide my steps as I continue to draw closer to you. Help me to see the sin in my life so I can eliminate it.

I want to rely on you, Lord, not myself. I fall short, I do not have all the answers, and I often fail. You, God, are perfect and have a perfect plan already carved out for me. I want your perfect plan for my life.

Help me to hear your voice and obey your calling.

Mute the whispers of doubt and lies in my head so I can clearly hear your direction.

Help me to fully rely on you in this area and all areas of my life.

Thank you, God, for your clear direction so that in honoring you, I can be blessed with all your Word promises, including conception. I am so grateful for your faithfulness.

I love you.

In Jesus' name,
Amen

Date: / /

Day 29: Taking Responsibility

When we do not get what we want, we get impatient and frustrated. We start looking for something or someone to blame. We need to take responsibility for what is in our control before lashing out at God about what we do not have.

SCRIPTURE

James 1:20, "for the anger of man does not produce the righteousness of God."

WHAT DOES GOD WANT FROM YOU?

Percentage of anger 0% ______ 100%

Today I am grateful for:

Today I take responsibility for:

How do you interact with God when you are angry or disappointed?

What effect does anger have in your life?

WHAT HAVE YOU BLAMED GOD FOR THAT IS REALLY YOUR RESPONSIBILITY?

TODAY'S CHECKLIST

- ▢ Read the Bible
- ▢ Pray
- ▢ Read TTCTF
- ▢ TTCTF Journal
- ▢ __________
- ▢ __________
- ▢ __________
- ▢ __________
- ▢ __________
- ▢ __________
- ▢ __________

NOTES

Date: / /

Day 30: Receiving Forgiveness Through Repentance

Our God forgives every time, but we have to repent. We have to commit to doing better, trying harder, and recognizing that this is a real relationship. We have to protect and honor it through repentance.

SCRIPTURE

1 John 1:9, "If we confess our sins, he is faithful and just to forgive us our sins and to cleanse us from all unrighteousness."

WHAT DOES GOD WANT FROM YOU?

Percentage of anger 0% ( ) 100%

Today I am grateful for:

Today I take responsibility for:

Why is it important to confess your sins to God?

Why is it hard for you to accept God's forgiveness of your sins?

WHAT SHOULD YOU REPENT FROM?

TODAY'S CHECKLIST

- ▢ Read the Bible
- ▢ Pray
- ▢ Read TTCTF
- ▢ TTCTF Journal
- ▢ ____________
- ▢ ____________
- ▢ ____________
- ▢ ____________
- ▢ ____________
- ▢ ____________
- ▢ ____________

NOTES

Date: / /

Day 31: Committing to Change

We need to stop getting sucked back into the same patterns that take away from our faith and instead trust in God. If we identify the patterns that lead us off of God's path, we can change them so we do not keep coming back to the same sins. If we do not change, our sin won't either.

SCRIPTURE

1 Corinthians 10:13, "No temptation has overtaken you that is not common to man. God is faithful, and he will not let you be tempted beyond your ability, but with the temptation he will also provide the way of escape, that you may be able to endure it."

WHAT DOES GOD WANT FROM YOU?

Percentage of anger 0% ( ) 100%

Today I am grateful for:

Today I take responsibility for:

What temptations overtake you and lead you to sin?

How does God help you overcome temptations?

WHAT CHANGES CAN YOU MAKE TODAY TO AVOID SIN?

TODAY'S CHECKLIST

- ▢ Read the Bible
- ▢ Pray
- ▢ Read TTCTF
- ▢ TTCTF Journal
- ▢ ______
- ▢ ______
- ▢ ______
- ▢ ______
- ▢ ______
- ▢ ______
- ▢ ______

NOTES

Date: / /

Day 32: Surrender Everything to God

We are praying for a baby, but God is asking for our hearts. If God isn't answering our prayers, maybe it is time to answer God first. That may require addressing sin we were not planning on dealing with today, but if we want God to bless us, we have to be willing to do whatever it takes.

SCRIPTURE

James 4:17, "So whoever knows the right thing to do and fails to do it, for him it is sin."

WHAT DOES GOD WANT FROM YOU?

Percentage of anger 0% ( ) 100%

Today I am grateful for:

Today I take responsibility for:

What does God want from you that you have been unwilling to do?

What would it take for you to surrender whatever God asks?

WHAT AREAS OF YOUR LIFE HAVE YOU NOT SURRENDERED TO GOD?

TODAY'S CHECKLIST

- ▢ Read the Bible
- ▢ Pray
- ▢ Read TTCTF
- ▢ TTCTF Journal
- ▢ __________
- ▢ __________
- ▢ __________
- ▢ __________
- ▢ __________
- ▢ __________
- ▢ __________

NOTES

Date: / /

Day 33: Forgiveness

If we are unwilling to forgive others, the Bible says we will not be able to receive forgiveness. The price of being uncomfortable for a few minutes to honor God is worth paying to receive complete forgiveness from God.

SCRIPTURE

Mark 11:25, "And whenever you stand praying, forgive, if you have anything against anyone, so that your Father also who is in heaven may forgive you your trespasses."

WHAT DOES GOD WANT FROM YOU?

Percentage of anger 0% ( ) 100%

Today I am grateful for:

Today I take responsibility for:

How has unforgiveness affected your relationship with God?

Who in your life do you need to forgive?

WHAT IS YOUR PLAN FOR FORGIVING OTHERS?

TODAY'S CHECKLIST

- ▢ Read the Bible
- ▢ Pray
- ▢ Read TTCTF
- ▢ TTCTF Journal
- ▢ ______
- ▢ ______
- ▢ ______
- ▢ ______
- ▢ ______
- ▢ ______
- ▢ ______

NOTES

Date: / /

Day 34: Trusting God's Plan

God has a plan for our lives, and even though we may have different plans, we have to trust him. We trust God by accepting that there is a purpose for this very moment in our lives. We trust that if God is letting us go through this season, we need to grow and take refuge in him.

SCRIPTURE

Psalm 18:2, "The LORD is my rock and my fortress and my deliverer, my God, my rock, in whom I take refuge, my shield, and the horn of my salvation, my stronghold."

WHAT DOES GOD WANT FROM YOU?

Percentage of anger 0% ( ) 100%

Today I am grateful for:

____

____

____

____

Today I take responsibility for:

____

____

____

____

Why is God worth trusting?

____

____

____

____

How are your plans silencing the voice of God?

____

____

____

____

____

HOW DO YOU TAKE REFUGE IN GOD AS YOU ARE TTCTF?

TODAY'S CHECKLIST

- ▢ Read the Bible
- ▢ Pray
- ▢ Read TTCTF
- ▢ TTCTF Journal
- ▢ ____________
- ▢ ____________
- ▢ ____________
- ▢ ____________
- ▢ ____________
- ▢ ____________
- ▢ ____________

NOTES

Date: / /

Day 35: God's Will

Sin distances us from God. If we accept sin in our lives, we are replacing God's control with our own. So what we may view as a small sin is still disobedience to God. We either follow our will or God's will.

SCRIPTURE

Ephesians 5:15-17, "Look carefully then how you walk, not as unwise but as wise, making the best use of the time, because the days are evil. Therefore do not be foolish, but understand what the will of the Lord is."

WHAT DOES GOD WANT FROM YOU?

Percentage of anger 0% ( ) 100%

Today I am grateful for:

Today I take responsibility for:

What sins in your life have you allowed that seem small but affect your walk?

How can you discern what the will of God is?

HOW ARE YOU WALKING WITH WISDOM WHILE TTCTF?

TODAY'S CHECKLIST

- ▢ Read the Bible
- ▢ Pray
- ▢ Read TTCTF
- ▢ TTCTF Journal
- ▢ ____________
- ▢ ____________
- ▢ ____________
- ▢ ____________
- ▢ ____________
- ▢ ____________
- ▢ ____________

NOTES

WEEK 6

UNITY IN MARRIAGE

GOAL

To love each other the way God defines love.

DAILY PRAYER

God, I know division does not come from you. I know you are the unifying bond that holds my marriage together. Through the good times and the bad times, you are the constant that guides us.

Through marriage, I have tied my heart and life to my husband, and the enemy continues to challenge me on this commitment. He tries to add bitterness, resentment, and anger. He tries to strip out love and replace it with his evil ways.

There is no place in my marriage for the king of division. I will no longer be deceived by the serpent. I will look to your Word for guidance, and I will seek your love for direction. I will set my heart on being a biblical wife. I will not let my emotions cloud my commitment that I made to my husband and to you, God.

I will serve you as his wife. I will serve him as his wife. I will honor you even when it is easier not to, because anything else is serving the enemy. Anything else let's the devil into our commitment. Anything else separates us from your unifying power.

Thank you for giving such clear instruction for my role as a wife in your Word.

Please help me to honor you.

Please help me to seek you in my marriage.

Please take this brokenness and use it to bring you glory.

Please let our unity produce fruit more precious than I could ever imagine. Thank you, Lord.

In Jesus' name,
Amen

Date: / /

Day 36: Recognizing Our Emotions

Emotions can make us read into something that is not really there; they bring up past hurts and other frustrations that do not belong. We need to learn how to differentiate between our feelings and facts, to help our marriages stay unified and honoring God.

SCRIPTURE

Matthew 19:6, "So they are no longer two but one flesh. What therefore God has joined together, let not man separate."

MY HUSBAND IS:

Percentage of patience 0% ______ 100%

Today I am grateful for:

Today, for my marriage, I will:

What is the hardest aspect of showing biblical love to your spouse when you are upset?

How could your last argument have been different if you were working on biblical love?

HOW CAN YOU CHANGE YOUR REACTIONS TO BE LOVING EVEN WHEN YOU ARE ANGRY OR MAD?

TODAY'S CHECKLIST

- ▢ Read the Bible
- ▢ Pray
- ▢ Read TTCTF
- ▢ TTCTF Journal
- ▢ ____________
- ▢ ____________
- ▢ ____________
- ▢ ____________
- ▢ ____________
- ▢ ____________
- ▢ ____________

NOTES

Date: / /

Day 37: Love No Matter What

We have to show love even when we do not feel loved if we want to obey God. Our commitment on our wedding day was not circumstantial; it included in "good times and bad." That commitment was not just made to our husbands; it was also made to God.

SCRIPTURE

1 Peter 3:1–2, "Likewise, wives, be subject to your own husbands, so that even if some do not obey the word, they may be won without a word by the conduct of their wives, when they see your respectful and pure conduct."

MY HUSBAND IS:

Percentage of patience 0% 100%

Today I am grateful for:

Today, for my marriage, I will:

How do you feel about receiving God's unconditional love?

How do you feel about showing biblical love to your husband?

WHEN IS THE HARDEST TIME TO SHOW BIBLICAL LOVE TO YOUR HUSBAND?

TODAY'S CHECKLIST

- ▢ Read the Bible
- ▢ Pray
- ▢ Read TTCTF
- ▢ TTCTF Journal
- ▢ ____________
- ▢ ____________
- ▢ ____________
- ▢ ____________
- ▢ ____________
- ▢ ____________
- ▢ ____________

NOTES

Date: / /

Day 38: Respecting the Roles God Gave

With so much emphasis on equality, our marriages have suffered. God gave us specific instructions for how to be a husband or wife. Until we embrace our differences, we will not have the marriages God intended us to have. Our marriages only honor God if we accept our God-given role.

SCRIPTURE

1 Corinthians 11:3, "But I want you to understand that the head of every man is Christ, the head of a wife is her husband, and the head of Christ is God."

MY HUSBAND IS:

Percentage of patience 0% ( ) 100%

Today I am grateful for:

Today, for my marriage, I will:

What problems come up when you do not accept the role God gave you as a wife?

How can you improve your role as a wife the way the Bible describes it?

THE HARDEST PART ABOUT BEING A GODLY WIFE IS:

TODAY'S CHECKLIST

- ▢ Read the Bible
- ▢ Pray
- ▢ Read TTCTF
- ▢ TTCTF Journal
- ▢ ____________
- ▢ ____________
- ▢ ____________
- ▢ ____________
- ▢ ____________
- ▢ ____________
- ▢ ____________

NOTES

Date: / /

Day 39: Being a Helper

Being the helper in our marriage does not mean we are less valuable than our husbands. It just means the role is different than leading. Two leaders cause confusion, chaos, and frustration which are all reasons why God gave us different roles. Instead of the chaos there is order and purpose when we maintain our God-given roles.

SCRIPTURE

Genesis 2:18, "Then the LORD God said, "It is not good that the man should be alone; I will make him a helper fit for him."

MY HUSBAND IS:

Percentage of patience 0% ( ) 100%

Today I am grateful for:

Today, for my marriage, I will:

How do you bring division in your marriage?

How do you bring unification in your marriage?

HOW CAN YOU ENSURE YOU ARE FOLLOWING GOD'S DIRECTION FOR BEING A GODLY WIFE?

TODAY'S CHECKLIST

- ▢ Read the Bible
- ▢ Pray
- ▢ Read TTCTF
- ▢ TTCTF Journal
- ▢ ______
- ▢ ______
- ▢ ______
- ▢ ______
- ▢ ______
- ▢ ______
- ▢ ______

NOTES

Date: / /

Day 40: Being Humble

Sometimes trusting and honoring God means we have to humble ourselves. We need to submit to his instructions even if we do not want to. When we trust the Lord enough to fully obey the Word as a wife, the changes that come from our obedience will be full of blessings.

SCRIPTURE

Ephesians 5:22-24, "Wives, submit to your own husbands, as to the Lord. For the husband is the head of the wife even as Christ is the head of the church, his body, and is himself its Savior. Now as the church submits to Christ, so also wives should submit in everything to their husbands."

MY HUSBAND IS:

Percentage of patience 0% 100%

Today I am grateful for:

Today, for my marriage, I will:

Can you ignore part of God's Word and still honor him? Why or why not?

How does obedience to God help you while you are TTCTF?

HOW CAN YOU HUMBLE YOURSELF TO IMPROVE YOUR MARRIAGE?

TODAY'S CHECKLIST

- ☐ Read the Bible
- ☐ Pray
- ☐ Read TTCTF
- ☐ TTCTF Journal
- ☐ ____
- ☐ ____
- ☐ ____
- ☐ ____
- ☐ ____
- ☐ ____
- ☐ ____

NOTES

Date: / /

Day 41: Forgiveness

No matter how long you have been married, there will be baggage. There is no perfect marriage because we are all imperfect people. Shoving two imperfect people together only multiplies problems, which is why forgiveness is necessary. If we forgive the past and focus on today, we will find joy, love, and so many blessings through honoring God.

SCRIPTURE

James 1:19–20, "Know this, my beloved brothers: let every person be quick to hear, slow to speak, slow to anger; for the anger of man does not produce the righteousness of God."

MY HUSBAND IS:

Percentage of patience 0% ______ 100%

Today I am grateful for:

Today, for my marriage, I will:

What is holding you back from forgiving in your marriage?

How can you stop keeping a record of wrongs in your marriage?

WRITE A LETTER TO YOUR HUSBAND ABOUT YOUR MARRIAGE:

TODAY'S CHECKLIST

- ▢ Read the Bible
- ▢ Pray
- ▢ Read TTCTF
- ▢ TTCTF Journal
- ▢ ____________
- ▢ ____________
- ▢ ____________
- ▢ ____________
- ▢ ____________
- ▢ ____________
- ▢ ____________

NOTES

Date: / /

Day 42: Pray for Your Marriage

It is vital that we pray for our marriages. When we pray for our marriages, we are reminded that God is who bound us together and he can bring unity through restoration, joy, hope, and so much love. When we pray, we stop leaning on our own abilities and gain access to God and his abilities. Without praying and seeking God, he is being left out of our marriages.

SCRIPTURE

Philippians 2:3, "Do nothing from selfish ambition or conceit, but in humility count others more significant than yourselves."

MY HUSBAND IS:

Percentage of patience 0% ______ 100%

Today I am grateful for:

Today, for my marriage, I will:

What are the weaknesses in your marriage?

What are the strengths in your marriage?

WRITE A PRAYER FOR YOUR MARRIAGE:

TODAY'S CHECKLIST

- ▢ Read the Bible
- ▢ Pray
- ▢ Read TTCTF
- ▢ TTCTF Journal
- ▢
- ▢
- ▢
- ▢
- ▢
- ▢
- ▢

NOTES

WEEK 7

HONORING THE BODY

GOAL

To honor your body as a gift from God.

DAILY PRAYER

God, I know this body is a gift, and I know I take it for granted. I know with all of its faults, it still has strengths. I know that as awesome as it is, I resent it for not being more.

But today, God, I realize that if I want more from this body, I have to love it. I have to take care of it. I have to honor it as the temple of your Holy Spirit.

I have tried many times, I have promised many times, and I have failed just as many.

Today, God, please help me change. Please help me see this body the way you see it. Please help me have the strength and the desire to honor this gift. I literally cannot do this without you.

This world has taught me that I am not enough if I am not perfect, but you, God, accept me in my flaws, and you shine in them. You take hold of my weaknesses and use them for your glory.

You are so good, God, that you can take something so broken and put it back together better than it ever was before.

Please restore this body and this mind. Please strengthen me to honor you by being diligent in taking care of this blessing. Every breath I breathe is by your design, your creation, and your purpose. Help me to see that goodness in myself; help me to not be deceived by the illusion of perfection, and help me to be encouraged by the work you have planned for me in this body.

Thank you for being my strength in this weakness. I love you, Lord.

In Jesus' name,
Amen

Date: / /

Day 43: Appreciating the Body

You may not be pregnant today, but you are living and breathing, and can be filled with hope from the promises in the Bible. This body is a gift and we cannot compare our bodies to other's. Find a way to love the gift of your body. With all of its flaws and imperfections, it is still a whole lot more than what we give it credit for.

SCRIPTURE

1 Corinthians 6:19–20, "Or do you not know that your body is a temple of the Holy Spirit within you, whom you have from God? You are not your own, for you were bought with a price. So glorify God in your body."

I LIKE MY BODY BECAUSE:

How much do you like your body 1-10?________

Today I am grateful for:

Today I will honor God with my body by:

How do you feel about your body being a temple of the Holy Spirit?

How can you accept your body as a gift?

LIST ALL THE STRENGTHS YOUR BODY HAS:

TODAY'S CHECKLIST

- ▢ Read the Bible
- ▢ Pray
- ▢ Read TTCTF
- ▢ TTCTF Journal
- ▢ ____________
- ▢ ____________
- ▢ ____________
- ▢ ____________
- ▢ ____________
- ▢ ____________
- ▢ ____________

NOTES

Date: / /

Day 44: Being Consistent

TTC occurs on a cyclical basis; there are two weeks of hope and two weeks of facing our reality. We cannot spend half of our time backsliding until it is time to hope again. We have to be fully committed to honoring God with our bodies. If we are not, we are sending a message that unless God gives us what we want, we will not take care of what we have.

SCRIPTURE

Proverbs 16:3, "Commit your work to the LORD, and your plans will be established."

I LIKE MY BODY BECAUSE:

How much do you like your body 1-10?________

Today I am grateful for:

____

____

____

____

Today I will honor God with my body by:

____

____

____

How can you be consistent with your health when you are not pregnant?

____

____

____

____

How does taking care of your body honor God?

____

____

____

____

LIST OTHER MOTIVATIONS TO TAKE CARE OF YOUR BODY:

TODAY'S CHECKLIST

- ▢ Read the Bible
- ▢ Pray
- ▢ Read TTCTF
- ▢ TTCTF Journal
- ▢ ____________
- ▢ ____________
- ▢ ____________
- ▢ ____________
- ▢ ____________
- ▢ ____________
- ▢ ____________

NOTES

Date: / /

Day 45: Eliminating Resentment

Resenting what we do not have will only make us bitter. If we trust God, we trust what we have is enough and that what God will give us will be even greater than what we imagined.

SCRIPTURE

Hebrews 12:15, "See to it that no one fails to obtain the grace of God; that no 'root of bitterness' springs up and causes trouble, and by it many become defiled;"

I LIKE MY BODY BECAUSE:

How much do you like your body 1-10?________

Today I am grateful for:

____

____

____

____

Today I will honor God with my body by:

____

____

____

____

____

What are you resentful of in your body?

____

____

____

____

How does bitterness affect your hope while you are TTCTF?

____

____

____

____

WHAT BRINGS YOU JOY TODAY?

TODAY'S CHECKLIST

- ▢ Read the Bible
- ▢ Pray
- ▢ Read TTCTF
- ▢ TTCTF Journal
- ▢ __________
- ▢ __________
- ▢ __________
- ▢ __________
- ▢ __________
- ▢ __________
- ▢ __________

NOTES

Date: / /

Day 46: Taking Care of Our Blessings

If we fail to take care of what we have been blessed with, how can we be trusted with more blessings? Children are one of the greatest, most important responsibilities. While we are TTCTF, it is important to work on where we are failing to honor God with what we have. If we take care of our blessings today, we will be trusted with more.

SCRIPTURE

Psalm 100:3, "Know that the LORD, he is God! It is he who made us, and we are his; we are his people, and the sheep of his pasture."

I LIKE MY BODY BECAUSE:

How much do you like your body 1-10?________

Today I am grateful for:

____

____

____

____

Today I will honor God with my body by:

____

____

____

____

How have you shown God you are trustworthy to receive more blessings?

____

____

____

____

How do you think God feels about the way you have taken care of your body?

____

____

____

____

WHAT IS THE HARDEST PART ABOUT TAKING CARE OF YOUR BODY?

TODAY'S CHECKLIST

- ▢ Read the Bible
- ▢ Pray
- ▢ Read TTCTF
- ▢ TTCTF Journal
- ▢ ____________
- ▢ ____________
- ▢ ____________
- ▢ ____________
- ▢ ____________
- ▢ ____________
- ▢ ____________

NOTES

Date: / /

Day 47: Eliminating the Bad

We have a choice, to make a change or to continue dishonoring God. Our bodies require work and intention to protect them. We need to commit to eliminating the bad habits we have in regards to eating, drinking, sleeping, and thinking, habits that work against our bodies' wellness.

SCRIPTURE

Romans 12:1, "I appeal to you therefore, brothers, by the mercies of God, to present your bodies as a living sacrifice, holy and acceptable to God, which is your spiritual worship."

I LIKE MY BODY BECAUSE:

How much do you like your body 1-10?________

Today I am grateful for:

Today I will honor God with my body by:

What is the biggest obstacle you face when trying to honor your body?

How can you get the strength to overcome the bad habits that dishonor God?

LIST WHAT YOU NEED TO ELIMINATE TO TAKE CARE OF YOUR BODY:

TODAY'S CHECKLIST

- ▢ Read the Bible
- ▢ Pray
- ▢ Read TTCTF
- ▢ TTCTF Journal
- ▢ ____________
- ▢ ____________
- ▢ ____________
- ▢ ____________
- ▢ ____________
- ▢ ____________
- ▢ ____________

NOTES

Date: / /

Day 48: Committing to the Good

We do not honor God if we do not take care of our blessings. When we finally accept our bodies as blessings, we will have a desire to take care of them, treasure them, and commit to doing whatever is necessary to replace bad habits with what pleases God.

SCRIPTURE

1 Corinthians 10:31, "So, whether you eat or drink, or whatever you do, do all to the glory of God."

I LIKE MY BODY BECAUSE:

How much do you like your body 1-10?________

Today I am grateful for:

____

____

____

____

Today I will honor God with my body by:

____

____

____

____

What do you think about your body?

____

____

____

____

Why is it important to make positive changes for your health while TTCTF?

____

____

____

____

____

I COMMIT TO IMPROVING MY HEALTH BY:

TODAY'S CHECKLIST

- ☐ Read the Bible
- ☐ Pray
- ☐ Read TTCTF
- ☐ TTCTF Journal
- ☐ ____________
- ☐ ____________
- ☐ ____________
- ☐ ____________
- ☐ ____________
- ☐ ____________
- ☐ ____________

NOTES

Date: / /

Day 49: Gratitude for All Blessings

When our expectations and realities do not match, painful emotions may come along with the disappointment. Thankfully, our reality is still so full of blessings. We need to make sure that our circumstances do not take away from all God has given us.

SCRIPTURE

1 Thessalonians 5:16–18, "Rejoice always, pray without ceasing, give thanks in all circumstances; for this is the will of God in Christ Jesus for you."

I LIKE MY BODY BECAUSE:

How much do you like your body 1-10?__________

Today I am grateful for:

Today I will honor God with my body by:

How does gratitude help your relationship with God?

How can you be grateful even when you do not have what you want?

WHAT OTHER BLESSINGS DO YOU TAKE FOR GRANTED?

TODAY'S CHECKLIST

- ▢ Read the Bible
- ▢ Pray
- ▢ Read TTCTF
- ▢ TTCTF Journal
- ▢ ______________
- ▢ ______________
- ▢ ______________
- ▢ ______________
- ▢ ______________
- ▢ ______________
- ▢ ______________

NOTES

WEEK 8

GOD'S PLAN

GOAL

To realizing God has a good plan and you can trust him no matter what his plan is.

DAILY PRAYER

God, I trust your plans for my life. I trust they are for good and not for harm. Time has passed by, and my plans have failed. I know if I do not make a change, they will continue to fail. I know, God, if I can surrender this broken heart, you can heal it completely.

Please help me surrender my plans.

Show me where to step, and I will step there. Show me where I am not obeying, and I will correct it.

Please make my will line up with your will. Make my plans your plans.

Please reveal to me when the questions in my mind and heart are causing doubt so I can eliminate all forms of doubt.

I trust in you and your timing. I trust that you are the answer to my prayers. I trust that your answer is "yes" because you have not told me "no."

I will seek you with my whole heart. I will know your Word and I will know your ways so I can be guarded against sin. I will rejoice in the waiting, in your timing, and in the testimony this journey will produce.

I will see mountains move in your name, and my faith will continue to grow. I believe you will answer this prayer, open my womb, and gift me with a healthy conceived child.

Thank you, God, for revelation and for answers to questions. I love you.

In Jesus' name,
Amen

Date: / /

Day 50: Trusting God's Plan Is Good

When we make plans, we do so based on our knowledge and understanding. When God makes plans, they are based on his knowledge, understanding, foresight, and wisdom. His plans are more trustworthy than ours will ever be, which means we can trust his plan even when we do not know what they are.

SCRIPTURE

Jeremiah 29:11–13, "For I know the plans I have for you, declares the LORD, plans for welfare and not for evil, to give you a future and a hope. Then you will call upon me and come and pray to me, and I will hear you. You will seek me and find me, when you seek me with all your heart."

HOW IS GOD'S PLAN GOOD?

Today I am grateful for:

Today I will trust God with:

How do you feel about God's plans?

Why can you trust God's plans without knowing what they are?

LIST WHY GOD IS A BETTER PLANNER THAN YOU ARE:

TODAY'S CHECKLIST

- ▢ Read the Bible
- ▢ Pray
- ▢ Read TTCTF
- ▢ TTCTF Journal
- ▢ ____________
- ▢ ____________
- ▢ ____________
- ▢ ____________
- ▢ ____________
- ▢ ____________
- ▢ ____________

NOTES

Date: / /

Day 51: Surrendering Your Plans

Surrendering our plans to God does not mean giving up on the desires of our hearts. It means trusting our desires to the one who can give them to us. It means trusting he knows better than we do. We need to pray for our wills to line up with God's will. We need to prayerfully seek God without letting our agenda get in the way.

SCRIPTURE

John 16:33, "I have said these things to you, that in me you may have peace. In the world you will have tribulation. But take heart; I have overcome the world."

HOW IS GOD'S PLAN GOOD?

Today I am grateful for:

Today I will trust God with:

What makes your plans flawed?

How does Jesus' overcoming the world give you peace about God's plan?

HOW CAN YOU SURRENDER YOUR PLANS FOR GOD'S?

TODAY'S CHECKLIST

- ▢ Read the Bible
- ▢ Pray
- ▢ Read TTCTF
- ▢ TTCTF Journal
- ▢
- ▢
- ▢
- ▢
- ▢
- ▢
- ▢

NOTES

Date: / /

Day 52: When Others Say No

Others may have told you no, but they are not God. God is the inventor of your uterus, your hormones, and all of the parts of the reproductive system. If something is broken, we get to go straight to the source, the inventor. We have to trust that with God all things are possible.

SCRIPTURE

Psalm 147:3, "He heals the brokenhearted and binds up their wounds."

HOW IS GOD'S PLAN GOOD?

Today I am grateful for:

____

____

____

____

Today I will trust God with:

____

____

____

____

____

Who else do you give authority to in your life, besides God? Why?

____

____

____

____

What is so broken in you that you believe God cannot restore?

____

____

____

____

LIST GOD'S LIMITATIONS AND STRENGTHS:

TODAY'S CHECKLIST

- ▢ Read the Bible
- ▢ Pray
- ▢ Read TTCTF
- ▢ TTCTF Journal
- ▢ ____________
- ▢ ____________
- ▢ ____________
- ▢ ____________
- ▢ ____________
- ▢ ____________
- ▢ ____________

NOTES

Date: / /

Day 53: Unrelenting in Pursuit

If we want God to answer us, relenting is not an option. Diligence leads to digging in, instead of giving up. If the desires of our hearts line up with God's Word, and we honor him by following the Bible, we can have the endurance to seek God, without relenting, to get pregnant.

SCRIPTURE

Proverbs 8:17, "I love those who love me, and those who seek me diligently find me."

HOW IS GOD'S PLAN GOOD?

Today I am grateful for:

Today I will trust God with:

How do the desires of your heart align with the Bible?

How would you describe your pursuit of God?

WHAT MAKES YOU STOP PURSUING GOD DILIGENTLY?

TODAY'S CHECKLIST

- ▢ Read the Bible
- ▢ Pray
- ▢ Read TTCTF
- ▢ TTCTF Journal
- ▢
- ▢
- ▢
- ▢
- ▢
- ▢
- ▢

NOTES

Date: / /

Day 54: Listening to God

The last thing we want to believe is the lies the enemy tries to plant in our minds and hearts. We need to be certain we only listen to the truth. Let our past be in the past. Let's trust that God has a great plan to be hopeful and joyful about.

SCRIPTURE

Luke 11:28, "But he said, 'Blessed rather are those who hear the word of God and keep it!'"

HOW IS GOD'S PLAN GOOD?

Today I am grateful for:

Today I will trust God with:

How can you evaluate if you are listening to God or lies?

What lies are you believing today?

WHY AFTER LISTENING TO GOD DO YOU HAVE TO ACT IN ORDER TO BE BLESSED?

TODAY'S CHECKLIST

- ▢ Read the Bible
- ▢ Pray
- ▢ Read TTCTF
- ▢ TTCTF Journal
- ▢ ______
- ▢ ______
- ▢ ______
- ▢ ______
- ▢ ______
- ▢ ______
- ▢ ______

NOTES

Date: / /

Day 55: Pleasing God

If we set our hearts to please God, our lives will be good and they will be fulfilled. God's expectations of us are more than a list of rules to follow; they are for our benefit. God designed us to thrive when we are pleasing him. When we please God, we live in his will and can receive his blessings.

SCRIPTURE

Hebrews 11:6, "And without faith it is impossible to please him, for whoever would draw near to God must believe that he exists and that he rewards those who seek him."

HOW IS GOD'S PLAN GOOD?

Today I am grateful for:

Today I will trust God with:

What is easy about pleasing God?

What is difficult about pleasing God?

WHAT CAN YOU DO DIFFERENTLY TO PLEASE GOD?

TODAY'S CHECKLIST

- ▢ Read the Bible
- ▢ Pray
- ▢ Read TTCTF
- ▢ TTCTF Journal
- ▢ ____________
- ▢ ____________
- ▢ ____________
- ▢ ____________
- ▢ ____________
- ▢ ____________
- ▢ ____________

NOTES

Date: / /

Day 56: Trusting God's Timing

There is nothing like wanting to be pregnant already and facing negative pregnancy tests over and over again. The only way to endure this hardship is to trust God and his timing—to trust that through him, we can receive this blessing and know that God has a purpose for why we are not pregnant yet.

SCRIPTURE

Psalm 27:14 (NIV), "Wait for the LORD; be strong and take heart and wait for the LORD."

HOW IS GOD'S PLAN GOOD?

Today I am grateful for:

Today I will trust God with:

What discourages you the most while you are TTC?

What does it mean to "be strong and take heart and wait for the LORD"?

WHAT GOOD HAS COME FROM YOUR TIME SPENT WAITING?

TODAY'S CHECKLIST

- ▢ Read the Bible
- ▢ Pray
- ▢ Read TTCTF
- ▢ TTCTF Journal
- ▢ ____________
- ▢ ____________
- ▢ ____________
- ▢ ____________
- ▢ ____________
- ▢ ____________
- ▢ ____________

NOTES

WEEK 9

FIGHTING DECEPTION

GOAL

To recognize deception and eliminate it so you only listen to God's truth.

DAILY PRAYER

God, I see the story of Eve, and the deception breaks my heart. She let one question cloud her trust in you, which changed the course of our lives today. That deception allowed sin to enter this world. Now here I stand before you, God, with doubts of my own. I am so sorry, God. I do not want my doubts to distort my trust in you. I do not want to question your promises, your Word, or your abilities.

I want to be stable in my walk with you.

If I continue in doubt, I see that I may not be able to receive this gift of conception. I see that doubt holds back blessings; it interferes with our relationship and even causes sin. I will eliminate the doubt in my life, God. I will stop listening to anything that is against your Word. If I have questions, I will go to your Word to look for answers.

I will not listen to lies.

I will no longer think or speak lies.

I will no longer be an easy target for manipulation by the enemy.

Please help me take captive every thought and make it obedient to you.

Thank you, God, for helping me to see through the deception. Thank you for turning this doubt into faith in you. Thank you, God, for allowing me to grow in you and ultimately for allowing me to conceive a child.

I am so grateful for your forgiveness. Thank you, God.

In Jesus' name,
Amen

Date: / /

Day 57: Facing the Lies

If we are not willing to admit we have been deceived, we will continue to be vulnerable to the control of the enemy. We need to prayerfully search our hearts to find any deception. Then we can face the lies and stop them from interfering with our relationship with God.

SCRIPTURE

Psalm 69:5, "O God, you know my folly; the wrongs I have done are not hidden from you."

THE ENEMY SNEAKS INTO MY LIFE BY:

Percentage of doubt 0% ________ 100%

Today I am grateful for:

Today I will listen to:

What false thoughts do you have when you are TTCTF?

What truthful thoughts do you have when you are TTCTF?

WHAT CAN YOU DO TO STOP BELIEVING LIES?

TODAY'S CHECKLIST

- ▢ Read the Bible
- ▢ Pray
- ▢ Read TTCTF
- ▢ TTCTF Journal
- ▢ ____________
- ▢ ____________
- ▢ ____________
- ▢ ____________
- ▢ ____________
- ▢ ____________
- ▢ ____________

NOTES

Date: / /

Day 58: Listen to the Truth

If we believe a lie, it feels like truth, which affects our perspective of the actual truth. Lies deceive us and cause us to distance ourselves from God. We need to be on guard for the thoughts in our heads. We need to prayerfully find out if our thoughts, feelings, or reasoning are based on the truth. We can only do so if we are letting the Spirit guide us.

SCRIPTURE

John 16:13, "When the Spirit of truth comes, he will guide you into all the truth..."

THE ENEMY SNEAKS INTO MY LIFE BY:

Percentage of doubt 0% ( ) 100%

Today I am grateful for:

Today I will listen to:

How can you focus on the facts without letting your feelings alter your perspective?

How do your emotions blind you from seeing the truth?

WHAT CAN YOU DO TO SEEK THE TRUTH?

TODAY'S CHECKLIST

- ▢ Read the Bible
- ▢ Pray
- ▢ Read TTCTF
- ▢ TTCTF Journal
- ▢ ______
- ▢ ______
- ▢ ______
- ▢ ______
- ▢ ______
- ▢ ______
- ▢ ______

NOTES

Date: / /

Day 59: Be On Guard for Deception

We need to understand that the enemy has a goal to deceive us. If we do not understand how the enemy targets us, we are more vulnerable to being deceived. The enemy wants to kill, steal, and destroy any hope we have in God. We need to be on guard against this deception so we can be strong in our faith and hope.

SCRIPTURE

1 Corinthians 16:13-14 (NLT), "Be on guard. Stand firm in the faith. Be courageous. Be strong. And do everything with love."

THE ENEMY SNEAKS INTO MY LIFE BY:

Percentage of doubt 0% ( ) 100%

Today I am grateful for:

Today I will listen to:

What makes you vulnerable to being deceived?

Who in your life plants seeds of deception?

HOW CAN YOU GUARD YOURSELF AGAINST DECEPTION?

TODAY'S CHECKLIST

- ▢ Read the Bible
- ▢ Pray
- ▢ Read TTCTF
- ▢ TTCTF Journal
- ▢ ____________
- ▢ ____________
- ▢ ____________
- ▢ ____________
- ▢ ____________
- ▢ ____________
- ▢ ____________

NOTES

Date: / /

Day 60: Accountability for Our Thoughts

We are responsible for all of our sins. Even if no one else in the world knows or sees them, God does. We have to hold ourselves to the standard God expects from us. We are accountable for our thoughts, words, and actions. We have to take captive our thoughts and ensure they line up with the Bible if we want to honor God.

SCRIPTURE

2 Corinthians 10:5 (NIV), "We demolish arguments and every pretension that sets itself up against the knowledge of God, and we take captive every thought to make it obedient to Christ."

THE ENEMY SNEAKS INTO MY LIFE BY:

Percentage of doubt 0% ( ) 100%

Today I am grateful for:

Today I will listen to:

How does the enemy use your thoughts to interfere when you are TTCTF?

Why does God care about your thoughts?

WHAT THOUGHTS DO YOU HAVE THAT TAKE AWAY FROM YOUR FAITH?

TODAY'S CHECKLIST

- ▢ Read the Bible
- ▢ Pray
- ▢ Read TTCTF
- ▢ TTCTF Journal
- ▢ ____________
- ▢ ____________
- ▢ ____________
- ▢ ____________
- ▢ ____________
- ▢ ____________
- ▢ ____________

NOTES

Date: / /

Day 61: Replacing Doubt With Faith

If we have faith, we will not doubt. If we are being deceived, we will be full of doubt. Doubt is a tool the enemy uses to break our faith and is often subtle. If we listen to doubt, it can grow. We cannot let doubt take root in us and therefore take away the blessings God has planned for us.

SCRIPTURE

James 1:6, "But let him ask in faith, with no doubting, for the one who doubts is like a wave of the sea that is driven and tossed by the wind."

THE ENEMY SNEAKS INTO MY LIFE BY:

Percentage of doubt 0% 100%

Today I am grateful for:

Today I will listen to:

How do doubts affect your faith?

What does God want from you before he can answer your prayers?

HOW CAN YOU RECOGNIZE DOUBTS AND STRENGTHEN YOUR FAITH?

TODAY'S CHECKLIST

- ▢ Read the Bible
- ▢ Pray
- ▢ Read TTCTF
- ▢ TTCTF Journal
- ▢ ____________
- ▢ ____________
- ▢ ____________
- ▢ ____________
- ▢ ____________
- ▢ ____________
- ▢ ____________

NOTES

Date: / /

Day 62: God's Protection

The enemy has been granted authority and power in this world, but God is more powerful and mighty. God guards us from the deception of our enemy. It is important that we pray for his protection while we are TTCTF.

SCRIPTURE

2 Thessalonians 3:3, "But the Lord is faithful. He will establish you and guard you against the evil one."

THE ENEMY SNEAKS INTO MY LIFE BY:

Percentage of doubt 0% ______ 100%

Today I am grateful for:

Today I will listen to:

How has God guarded you in the past against the evil one?

How does it feel to be guarded from God while you are TTCTF?

HOW DOES GOD'S FAITHFULNESS PROTECT YOU FROM THE POWER AND AUTHORITY OF SATAN?

TODAY'S CHECKLIST

- ☐ Read the Bible
- ☐ Pray
- ☐ Read TTCTF
- ☐ TTCTF Journal
- ☐ ____________
- ☐ ____________
- ☐ ____________
- ☐ ____________
- ☐ ____________
- ☐ ____________
- ☐ ____________

NOTES

Date: / /

Day 63: Humility and Grace

When we are willing to face our deception and admit we are wrong, God gives us grace. If we are not willing to humble ourselves, not only are we without God's grace, we also have God opposing us! Let's make sure we are on God's side so we can receive his grace and benefit from not being deceived.

SCRIPTURE

James 4:6, "...God opposes the proud but gives grace to the humble."

THE ENEMY SNEAKS INTO MY LIFE BY:

Percentage of doubt 0% ( ) 100%

Today I am grateful for:

Today I will listen to:

How will humbling yourself help you hear more from God?

What are you doing that opposes God when you are TTCTF?

LIST THE PRIDEFUL AREAS IN YOUR LIFE THAT YOU NEED TO SURRENDER TO GOD:

TODAY'S CHECKLIST

- ▢ Read the Bible
- ▢ Pray
- ▢ Read TTCTF
- ▢ TTCTF Journal
- ▢
- ▢
- ▢
- ▢
- ▢
- ▢
- ▢

NOTES

WEEK 10

TRUSTING GOD

GOAL

To ensure you trust God in all circumstances because he is worthy of your trust.

DAILY PRAYER

God, in my imperfection you wait. In my frustration, you wait. In my disobedience, you wait. As this life goes by, you continue to wait, Lord.

You are the God of love, who is patient and kind. In my waiting, I have been just the opposite. I have grown resentful, bitter, and my heart has hardened.

It hurts to keep feeling such a deep longing. It hurts to know that you are not answering this prayer even though I know you can. But, God, it hurts even more to realize that you want to bless me with a baby and I have held you back. Instead of digging deeper into you, I drifted further away. I have separated myself from you in my pain.

I have let my wants, desires, and dreams affect my relationship with you. I am sorry, God. Please restore this bitter, broken heart.

God, I know you are the same yesterday, today, and forever. I also know that my ways are not your ways, and my thoughts are not your thoughts. I know if you are waiting, you have a reason.

I will trust in your timing. I will trust in your purpose for this season. I will grow.

Please search my heart, God. Show me how to trust you. Show me how to dig deeper. Show me where I am outside of your will so I can get back on your path.

Thank you, God, for your patience in waiting on me. I love you, Lord.

In Jesus' name,
Amen

Date: / /

Day 64: When God Rewards Us

God has a reward system for his children. As God's children, we are held to a standard that requires us to put work into pleasing God. The gift of salvation even requires us to act; we have to accept this gift. If we recognize our limitations surrounding each biblical promise and work on those weaknesses, God will reward us through our efforts and faith.

SCRIPTURE

Psalm 127:3, "Behold, children are a heritage from the LORD, the fruit of the womb a reward."

HOW MUCH DO YOU TRUST GOD?

Color in the pie chart with the percentage of trust you have in God.

Today I am grateful for:

___

___

___

___

Today I trust God because:

___

___

___

___

How are you growing in your walk with God?

___

___

___

___

How are you seeking God for answers?

___

___

___

___

WHAT IN YOUR LIFE IS OUTSIDE OF GOD'S WILL THAT IS HOLDING BACK GOD FROM REWARDING YOU?

TODAY'S CHECKLIST

- ▢ Read the Bible
- ▢ Pray
- ▢ Read TTCTF
- ▢ TTCTF Journal
- ▢ __________
- ▢ __________
- ▢ __________
- ▢ __________
- ▢ __________
- ▢ __________
- ▢ __________

NOTES

Date: / /

Day 65: Patience in Tribulation

We get impatient when pregnancy has not happened in our timing and according to our plan. Waiting to get pregnant is a time-sensitive prayer request. We have a window each month during ovulation in which we can get pregnant. Once that time passes, all we can do is wait. If we choose peace, that frustration will be eliminated. We can only have peace if we are patiently trusting in God and in his plan with our prayer requests.

SCRIPTURE

Romans 12:12, "Rejoice in hope, be patient in tribulation, be constant in prayer."

HOW MUCH DO YOU TRUST GOD?

Color in the pie chart with the percentage of trust you have in God.

Today I am grateful for:

Today I trust God because:

How does the trial of TTCTF affect your patience?

How can there be good that comes from waiting while TTCTF?

HOW CAN YOU MINIMIZE FRUSTRATION WHILE YOU ARE TTCTF?

TODAY'S CHECKLIST

- ▢ Read the Bible
- ▢ Pray
- ▢ Read TTCTF
- ▢ TTCTF Journal
- ▢ ____
- ▢ ____
- ▢ ____
- ▢ ____
- ▢ ____
- ▢ ____
- ▢ ____

NOTES

Date: / /

Day 66: God Is Capable

We can be patient while TTCTF if we understand that God is capable of answering our prayers. Patience is a sign of trust, and God has earned our trust. He has shown us over and over again in the Bible that he is capable of answering our prayers. To grow our trust, we need to understand that our limitations do not apply to God.

SCRIPTURE

Luke 1:37, "For nothing will be impossible with God."

HOW MUCH DO YOU TRUST GOD?

Color in the pie chart with the percentage of trust you have in God.

Today I am grateful for:

Today I trust God because:

What does your impatience communicate to God while you are TTCTF?

What makes you lose hope when you are TTCTF?

WHAT MAKES GOD CAPABLE OF ANSWERING YOUR PRAYERS?

TODAY'S CHECKLIST

- ▢ Read the Bible
- ▢ Pray
- ▢ Read TTCTF
- ▢ TTCTF Journal
- ▢ ____________
- ▢ ____________
- ▢ ____________
- ▢ ____________
- ▢ ____________
- ▢ ____________
- ▢ ____________

NOTES

Date: / /

Day 67: Constant in Prayer

We get to communicate with God at any time and in any moment through prayer. When we are ready, he will listen. But God does so much more than listen; he provides answers, direction, and wisdom. When we stop praying and communicating with God, we are on our own and we are not enough when TTCTF.

SCRIPTURE

1 Thessalonians 5:16–18, "Rejoice always, pray without ceasing, give thanks in all circumstances; for this is the will of God in Christ Jesus for you."

HOW MUCH DO YOU TRUST GOD?

Color in the pie chart with the percentage of trust you have in God.

Today I am grateful for:

Today I trust God because:

How is it possible to be constant in prayer?

What can you do to create a prayer habit?

HOW CAN PRAYING BE YOUR FIRST RESPONSE WHEN TTCTF?

TODAY'S CHECKLIST

- ▢ Read the Bible
- ▢ Pray
- ▢ Read TTCTF
- ▢ TTCTF Journal
- ▢
- ▢
- ▢
- ▢
- ▢
- ▢
- ▢

NOTES

Date: / /

Day 68: Praying in All Occasions

We cannot be conditional in our prayer life. We have to pray to God when we are happy, sad, mad, hurt, broken, and more. God wants our good and our bad so he can help us to be better. The more we learn and grow, the more prepared we will be for what comes next.

SCRIPTURE

Ephesians 6:18 (NIV), "And pray in the Spirit on all occasions with all kinds of prayers and requests."

HOW MUCH DO YOU TRUST GOD?

Color in the pie chart with the percentage of trust you have in God.

Today I am grateful for:

Today I trust God because:

On what occasions do you find yourself praying most to God?

When is the hardest time for you to pray to God?

HOW CAN YOU BE CONSISTENT IN YOUR PRAYER LIFE NO MATTER WHAT THE CIRCUMSTANCES ARE?

TODAY'S CHECKLIST

- ▢ Read the Bible
- ▢ Pray
- ▢ Read TTCTF
- ▢ TTCTF Journal
- ▢ ____________
- ▢ ____________
- ▢ ____________
- ▢ ____________
- ▢ ____________
- ▢ ____________
- ▢ ____________

NOTES

Date: / /

Day 69: Rejoice in Hope

Every month we are TTCTF is followed by a definitive yes or no of pregnancy. We need to find a way to rejoice in God and his promises while we wait for his plan and timing, regardless of the outcome. We have to remember that we can hope because God is faithful.

SCRIPTURE

Psalm 130:5-6, "I wait for the LORD, my soul waits, and in his word I hope; my soul waits for the LORD more than watchmen for the morning, more than watchmen for the morning."

HOW MUCH DO YOU TRUST GOD?

Color in the pie chart with the percentage of trust you have in God.

Today I am grateful for:

Today I trust God because:

How can you rejoice when your prayers are not answered yet?

How can you have consistent hope in the promises God has given?

HOW CAN YOU REJOICE AS YOU ARE WAITING IN THE HOPES OF HAVING A BABY?

TODAY'S CHECKLIST

- ▢ Read the Bible
- ▢ Pray
- ▢ Read TTCTF
- ▢ TTCTF Journal
- ▢ ______
- ▢ ______
- ▢ ______
- ▢ ______
- ▢ ______
- ▢ ______
- ▢ ______

NOTES

Date: / /

Day 70: Trusting in All Circumstances

Our circumstances do not change who God is and what he is capable of! God is faithful, even when we are faithless. We can trust him even when we cannot trust ourselves. We need to ensure our trust is consistent.

SCRIPTURE

1 Peter 5:7, “Casting all your anxieties on him, because he cares for you.”

HOW MUCH DO YOU TRUST GOD?

Color in the pie chart with the percentage of trust you have in God.

Today I am grateful for:

Today I trust God because:

What is difficult about trusting God?

What is easy about trusting God?

HOW DOES KNOWING GOD CARES FOR YOU HELP YOU HAVE PEACE?

TODAY'S CHECKLIST

- ▢ Read the Bible
- ▢ Pray
- ▢ Read TTCTF
- ▢ TTCTF Journal
- ▢ ____________
- ▢ ____________
- ▢ ____________
- ▢ ____________
- ▢ ____________
- ▢ ____________
- ▢ ____________

NOTES

WEEK 11

IMPERFECT ACTION

GOAL

To take action without getting overwhelmed by your shortcomings so you grow in your relationship with God, no matter what you face.

DAILY PRAYER

God, knowing that I am going to fail scares me. I do not want to fail. I do not want to be outside of your will.

I feel like I am already starting from behind. I desperately need you to fill the void of my shortcomings. My heart aches to serve you wholeheartedly, but my flesh fails constantly.

I reach for mountains and end up in a pit, but you, my God, are the God who moves mountains. Your clarity and your peace are worth searching for. Your love and your direction are the only guides I need in this life. I know you sent Jesus because you know of my faults and failures.

Through faith, not perfection, I see all things are possible.

My faith in you continues to grow, and I will keep taking action to align my will with your will.

I continue to hope in your plans and purpose in this imperfect life. I am completely trusting that in my weakness, you will shine the brightest.

Please use my weaknesses for your glory so that in my efforts to obey your Word, I can receive your blessings.

Thank you, Lord, for using this season to produce a closer relationship with you, for pregnancy, and for helping me to be a godly parent.

Your perfection makes all of this possible. Thank you, God.

In Jesus' name,
Amen

Date: / /

Day 71: Facing Imperfections

Sin impacts our walk with God and takes us away from the plan God has for us. Instead of being discouraged by our faults, we can use our sin as motivation to be better. This motivation can improve our walk with God and help us grow closer to him. By facing our imperfections, we position ourselves more in line with God's will, which honors him.

SCRIPTURE

Romans 3:23, "for all have sinned and fall short of the glory of God..."

WHAT ARE YOU DOING WELL?

Today I am grateful for:

Today I will work on:

How can God help you where you fall short?

How can understanding your sin be a motivator while you are TTCTF?

HOW CAN YOU STILL GLORIFY GOD IN YOUR SHORTCOMINGS?

TODAY'S CHECKLIST

- ▢ Read the Bible
- ▢ Pray
- ▢ Read TTCTF
- ▢ TTCTF Journal
- ▢ ______
- ▢ ______
- ▢ ______
- ▢ ______
- ▢ ______
- ▢ ______
- ▢ ______

NOTES

Date: / /

Day 72: Eliminating Jealousy

There will always be others who have what we do not. What they have does not add or subtract to what we have. We have God, who has provided us with all that we have and all we will ever have or need. Jealousy is not a fruit of the Spirit. God owes us nothing, and yet he gives us so much. God will bless us if we continue to honor and obey his Word.

How often do you struggle with jealousy?

SCRIPTURE

James 3:16, "For where jealousy and selfish ambition exist, there will be disorder and every vile practice."

WHAT ARE YOU DOING WELL?

Today I am grateful for:

Today I will work on:

How do you feel about God blessing others?

What are you missing out on by being jealous of others?

WHAT CAN YOU DO WHEN YOU START FEELING JEALOUS OF OTHERS?

TODAY'S CHECKLIST

- ▢ Read the Bible
- ▢ Pray
- ▢ Read TTCTF
- ▢ TTCTF Journal
- ▢ ____________
- ▢ ____________
- ▢ ____________
- ▢ ____________
- ▢ ____________
- ▢ ____________
- ▢ ____________

NOTES

Date: / /

Day 73: Being a Doer

When we understand that we are not living according to God's plan, we are obligated to make a change. When we do not act in obedience, how can we expect to be blessed? When we find inconsistencies between our lives and what the Bible says, we have to make the necessary changes so we are also being doers.

SCRIPTURE

James 1:25, "But the one who looks into the perfect law, the law of liberty, and perseveres, being no hearer who forgets but a doer who acts, he will be blessed in his doing."

WHAT ARE YOU DOING WELL?

Today I am grateful for:

Today I will work on:

What have you not been doing that God expects of you?

What do you need to do to have a better relationship with God?

WHAT CAN YOU DO TO PERSEVERE SO YOU CAN BE BLESSED THROUGH YOUR ACTIONS?

TODAY'S CHECKLIST

- ▢ Read the Bible
- ▢ Pray
- ▢ Read TTCTF
- ▢ TTCTF Journal
- ▢ ____________
- ▢ ____________
- ▢ ____________
- ▢ ____________
- ▢ ____________
- ▢ ____________
- ▢ ____________

NOTES

Date: / /

Day 74: Facing the Mountain With God

An empty womb will always be a gigantic mountain when we face it alone. On our own, we are not enough. We have to face this mountain with God. God is what makes the mountain obsolete. His greatness is not just because he is so much bigger than our problems; he is the answer to our problems. If we are focused on God, all that we lack will be filled with his power, strength, and blessings.

SCRIPTURE

Psalm 73:26, "My flesh and my heart may fail, but God is the strength of my heart and my portion forever."

WHAT ARE YOU DOING WELL?

Today I am grateful for:

Today I will work on:

When do you rely on yourself instead of God?

How do you lean on God to be your strength?

WHAT IMPROVEMENTS DO YOU NOTICE WHEN YOU ARE RELYING ON GOD WHILE TTCTF?

TODAY'S CHECKLIST

- ☐ Read the Bible
- ☐ Pray
- ☐ Read TTCTF
- ☐ TTCTF Journal
- ☐
- ☐
- ☐
- ☐
- ☐
- ☐
- ☐

NOTES

Date: / /

Day 75: God Provides Direction

We have to look for God's direction, not just for the answer we want to hear. When God is directing us, we do not necessarily see the big picture. Thankfully, he gives us the lamp at our feet to see what to do next. We can trust the step he is showing us while believing that his guidance will get us to the blessings we are searching for.

SCRIPTURE

Psalm 119:105, "Your word is a lamp to my feet and a light to my path."

WHAT ARE YOU DOING WELL?

Today I am grateful for:

Today I will work on:

How are you searching God for guidance while you are TTCTF?

Why is a lamp at your feet enough to guide you as you are TTCTF?

HOW DO YOUR SINS AFFECT SEEING GOD'S DIRECTION?

TODAY'S CHECKLIST

- ▢ Read the Bible
- ▢ Pray
- ▢ Read TTCTF
- ▢ TTCTF Journal
- ▢
- ▢
- ▢
- ▢
- ▢
- ▢
- ▢

NOTES

Date: / /

Day 76: Accepting Hardship as Discipline

God wants us to grow. If we face hardships and do not grow from them, then we are not learning or changing what he wants. While we are TTCTF, we need to make sure we learn and grow so this season not only has purpose but also helps prepare us for what is to come.

SCRIPTURE

Hebrews 12:7 (NIV), "Endure hardship as discipline; God is treating you as his children."

WHAT ARE YOU DOING WELL?

Today I am grateful for:

Today I will work on:

How do you feel about being God's child?

How do you feel about being disciplined by God?

HOW CAN YOU BENEFIT FROM GOD'S DISCIPLINE?

TODAY'S CHECKLIST

- ▢ Read the Bible
- ▢ Pray
- ▢ Read TTCTF
- ▢ TTCTF Journal
- ▢ ____________
- ▢ ____________
- ▢ ____________
- ▢ ____________
- ▢ ____________
- ▢ ____________
- ▢ ____________

NOTES

Date: / /

Day 77: Finding Blessings in All Seasons

God is glorified in our weaknesses. This season prepares us, it molds us, and it grows us so we can be even better moms than we ever imagined. If we grow here, we will be more prepared for what is to come. We need to let this season have its purpose to prepare us for the next season. This happens by obeying God's Word today.

SCRIPTURE

Hebrews 12:11 (NIV), "No discipline seems pleasant at the time, but painful. Later on, however, it produces a harvest of righteousness and peace for those who have been trained by it."

WHAT ARE YOU DOING WELL?

Today I am grateful for:

Today I will work on:

What else can your TTCTF journey produce besides a baby?

How can the pain you face today produce peace in your future?

HOW ARE YOU GLORIFYING GOD WHILE TTCTF?

TODAY'S CHECKLIST

- ☐ Read the Bible
- ☐ Pray
- ☐ Read TTCTF
- ☐ TTCTF Journal
- ☐ ____________
- ☐ ____________
- ☐ ____________
- ☐ ____________
- ☐ ____________
- ☐ ____________
- ☐ ____________

NOTES

WEEK 12

BIBLICAL INFERTILITY

GOAL

To remember the biblical evidence of God answering prayers for conceiving and remembering our circumstances do not change God's ability.

DAILY PRAYER

Thank you, God, for your Word and for reminding me that you are the God who answers prayers. You are the God who has no limitations.

Thank you for caring about my broken heart, and thank you for being able and willing to answer this prayer. I want to honor and obey you with my life.

Please show me your will.

Please reveal what I can do to get pregnant. Reveal when I am listening to lies so I can find your truth in all of my thoughts and actions. Show me how infertility is not an obstacle for you.

I commit to obeying your direction and honoring you completely.

I trust you, I hope in you, and I am committed to serving you.

Please restore the joy and hope in my heart.

Please open my womb and allow me to conceive a baby as you have done for Sarah, Rebekah, Rachel, Manoah's wife, Hannah, the Shunammite woman, and Elizabeth. I believe you have shown me over and over again that you have authority over the womb to restore my hope in answering this prayer.

Thank you, Lord, for hearing my prayers and loving me even through my struggles.

I love you, God!

In Jesus' name,
Amen

Date: / /

Day 78: Sarah

Not only was Sarah older in age when she finally had confirmation she would bear a son but she had a hard time believing it was true. She even laughed at the idea. Thankfully, her doubt did not stop God's plan. God blessed her anyway.

SCRIPTURE

Genesis 18:10, "The LORD said, 'I will surely return to you about this time next year, and Sarah your wife shall have a son.'"

WHO WAS SARAH'S CHILD?

Today I am grateful for:

Today I know God can answer my prayers because:

How do your circumstances cause you to doubt God?

What help can you accept from your husband while TTCTF?

WHAT ARE YOU DOING OR SAYING THAT UNINTENTIONALLY REVEALS YOU ARE DOUBTING GOD?

TODAY'S CHECKLIST

- ☐ Read the Bible
- ☐ Pray
- ☐ Read TTCTF
- ☐ TTCTF Journal
- ☐ __________
- ☐ __________
- ☐ __________
- ☐ __________
- ☐ __________
- ☐ __________
- ☐ __________

NOTES

Date: / /

Day 79: Rebekah

In the case of Rebekah, God listened to her husband Isaac's prayers for pregnancy. Rebekah conceived. This reveals how important it is for us to pray with our husbands, honor God, and obey his Word.

SCRIPTURE

Genesis 25:21, "And Isaac prayed to the LORD for his wife, because she was barren. And the LORD granted his prayer, and Rebekah his wife conceived."

WHO WERE REBEKAH'S CHILDREN?

Today I am grateful for:

Today I know God can answer my prayers because:

What is your plan for praying with your husband?

What are you doing that is hurting your marriage while TTCTF?

WHAT SUPPORT DO YOU NEED FROM YOUR HUSBAND WHILE TTCTF?

TODAY'S CHECKLIST

- ▢ Read the Bible
- ▢ Pray
- ▢ Read TTCTF
- ▢ TTCTF Journal
- ▢ ____________
- ▢ ____________
- ▢ ____________
- ▢ ____________
- ▢ ____________
- ▢ ____________
- ▢ ____________

NOTES

Date: / /

Day 80: Rachel

God listened to Rachel. He listened, he opened her womb, and she conceived. If she had not been speaking to God and seeking him, it is possible she never would have conceived a child.

SCRIPTURE

Genesis 30:22-23, "Then God remembered Rachel, and God listened to her and opened her womb. She conceived and bore a son and said, 'God has taken away my reproach.'"

WHO WERE RACHEL'S CHILDREN?

Today I am grateful for:

Today I know God can answer my prayers because:

How are you seeking God while TTCTF?

How are you being consistent with your relationship with God?

HOW CAN YOU MAKE SURE GOD REMEMBERS YOU WHILE YOU ARE TTCTF?

TODAY'S CHECKLIST

- ▢ Read the Bible
- ▢ Pray
- ▢ Read TTCTF
- ▢ TTCTF Journal
- ▢ ____________
- ▢ ____________
- ▢ ____________
- ▢ ____________
- ▢ ____________
- ▢ ____________
- ▢ ____________

NOTES

Date: / /

Day 81: Manoah's Wife

The mother of Samson was barren, but God allowed her to conceive. Through her conception, God grew a strong man who ultimately defeated many of the Philistines who were against God's people. God has a plan for all of our lives, even those whom are not yet conceived.

SCRIPTURE

Judges 13:24, "And the woman bore a son and called his name Samson. And the young man grew, and the LORD blessed him."

WHO WAS MANOAH'S SON?

Today I am grateful for:

Today I know God can answer my prayers because:

How can you find peace about the plans God has for your child in this world?

Why does the enemy not want you to conceive?

WHAT POTENTIAL BLESSINGS ARE MISSED WHEN WE DO NOT HAVE FAITH IN GOD?

TODAY'S CHECKLIST

- ▢ Read the Bible
- ▢ Pray
- ▢ Read TTCTF
- ▢ TTCTF Journal
- ▢ ____________
- ▢ ____________
- ▢ ____________
- ▢ ____________
- ▢ ____________
- ▢ ____________
- ▢ ____________

NOTES

Date: / /

Day 82: Hannah

Hannah's husband loved her even though they were unable to conceive. He took care of her and provided more for her than he did for others. While TTCTF, we need to look for the love we have today and make sure we are not neglecting our marriages.

SCRIPTURE

1 Samuel 1:5, "But to Hannah he gave a double portion, because he loved her, though the LORD had closed her womb."

WHO WAS HANNAH'S FIRST CHILD?

How many children did Hannah have? ______

Today I am grateful for:

______
______
______
______

Today I know God can answer my prayers because:

______
______
______
______

How can you make sure you are not neglecting your marriage today?

______
______
______
______

How can you make love a priority in your marriage while you are TTCTF?

______
______
______
______
______

WHAT DOES YOUR HUSBAND DO TO SHOW YOU HE LOVES YOU?

TODAY'S CHECKLIST

- ▢ Read the Bible
- ▢ Pray
- ▢ Read TTCTF
- ▢ TTCTF Journal
- ▢ ______
- ▢ ______
- ▢ ______
- ▢ ______
- ▢ ______
- ▢ ______
- ▢ ______

NOTES

Date: / /

Day 83: The Shunammite Woman

The Shunammite woman's husband was old in age, but that did not stop God from giving them a baby. God does not see the obstacles we see; whether it is age or health issues, God has the answer and provides.

SCRIPTURE

2 Kings 4:14, "Gehazi answered, 'Well, she has no son, and her husband is old.'"

HOW DID HER KINDNESS HELP HER?

Today I am grateful for:

Today I know God can answer my prayers because:

What physical obstacles are you facing while TTCTF?

How can God work around your obstacles?

HOW DOES YOUR HUSBAND'S CIRCUMSTANCES AFFECT YOUR FAITH IN GOD ANSWERING THIS PRAYER?

TODAY'S CHECKLIST

- ▢ Read the Bible
- ▢ Pray
- ▢ Read TTCTF
- ▢ TTCTF Journal
- ▢ ______
- ▢ ______
- ▢ ______
- ▢ ______
- ▢ ______
- ▢ ______
- ▢ ______

NOTES

Date: / /

Day 84: Elizabeth

God had big plans for Elizabeth's son. They were told that he would turn many of Israel's children to the Lord. Even with these big plans, the angel also told her husband, Zechariah, that their son would bring them joy and gladness.

SCRIPTURE

Luke 1:14, "And you will have joy and gladness, and many will rejoice at his birth..."

WHO WAS ELIZABETH'S CHILD?

Today I am grateful for:

Today I know God can answer my prayers because:

Why do you think God has joy planned for you?

How is God providing joy and gladness in your life today?

WHY CAN YOU TRUST GOD'S PLAN FOR YOUR CHILD?

TODAY'S CHECKLIST

- ▢ Read the Bible
- ▢ Pray
- ▢ Read TTCTF
- ▢ TTCTF Journal
- ▢
- ▢
- ▢
- ▢
- ▢
- ▢
- ▢

NOTES

WEEK 13

GOD IS FAITHFUL

GOAL

To remember our lack of faith does not change God's faithfulness and understanding, that when we are faithful, God answers prayers.

DAILY PRAYER

God, throughout my doubt, my brokenness, my hurt, my pain, and my anger, you have been faithful. You have been faithful to me, to your Word, and to the promises you have given. You have never wavered. Even though I questioned and lost faith, you remained the same.

Now, God, my faith is growing, and my hope is solidifying in you, your plans, and your ways. Throughout this growth, you have continued to be patient, waiting for me to reach out and trust you.

I trust you, God.

I trust you hear this prayer and you are continuing to work in me.

I trust you will continue to guide me and show me where I need to grow and what I need to do to obey your Word. I trust you will answer this prayer according to your Word to get pregnant.

Please, God, open this womb; let me conceive a child. Let this child be completely healthy, grow to full term, and come out at your timing, ready to face this world with parents who are renewed in their faith and love for you.

Let all of the brokenness I have endured be replaced with the everlasting joy of motherhood. You have remained faithful in my unfaithfulness. I am so excited to see what you are able to do in my faith.

Thank you, God, for hearing and answering my prayers.

Thank you for being the God of miracles.

Thank you for your great love for me.

Thank you for renewing my hope and faith.

Thank you, God, for showing me where I was holding your hands back from blessing me. Thank you, God, for forgiving me.

I truly love you, Lord. You are the King on the throne, and your greatness is beyond anything I could imagine. I am in awe that something so big to me is something so easy for you. I love you, and I will continue to walk in faith, trusting your timing.

To you, God, be the glory, forever and ever,
Amen

Date: / /

Day 85: Growing With God

God gave us life to honor and glorify him. As God's children, we are expected to do just that. It is up to us to keep growing with God instead of going through this life on our own. When we choose our ways without considering God's, we are not growing in God's knowledge and grace.

SCRIPTURE

2 Peter 3:18, "But grow in the grace and knowledge of our Lord and Savior Jesus Christ. To him be the glory both now and to the day of eternity. Amen."

MARK WHERE YOU ARE TODAY

Heartache 0% [ ] 100%

Hope 0% [ ] 100%

Determination 0% [ ] 100%

Today I am grateful for:

___

___

___

___

Today God has shown me his faithfulness by:

___

___

___

___

What does God expect from you as his child?

___

___

___

___

What is your purpose in life?

___

___

___

___

___

DESCRIBE YOUR RELATIONSHIP WITH GOD:

TODAY'S CHECKLIST

- ▢ Read the Bible
- ▢ Pray
- ▢ Read TTCTF
- ▢ TTCTF Journal
- ▢
- ▢
- ▢
- ▢
- ▢
- ▢
- ▢

NOTES

Date: / /

Day 86: Enduring Trials Through Perseverance

We need perseverance because TTCTF is hard. It is a trial, and to get through it with our sanity, our endurance requires strength that only comes from trusting and having faith in God. The ups and downs will try to take away from our faith, but God is bigger, so we have to be motivated by the desires of our hearts to persevere through faith.

SCRIPTURE

James 1:3–4 (NIV), "...the testing of your faith produces perseverance. Let perseverance finish its work so that you may be mature and complete, not lacking anything."

MARK WHERE YOU ARE TODAY

Anger 0% ________ 100%

Resentment 0% ________ 100%

Happiness 0% ________ 100%

Today I am grateful for:

____

____

____

____

Today God has shown me his faithfulness by:

____

____

____

____

How has your faith in God endured as you have waited for conception?

____

____

____

____

How has your hope endured as you have waited for conception?

____

____

____

____

HOW DOES YOUR PERSEVERANCE HELP YOU BECOME COMPLETE?

TODAY'S CHECKLIST

- ▢ Read the Bible
- ▢ Pray
- ▢ Read TTCTF
- ▢ TTCTF Journal
- ▢ ____________
- ▢ ____________
- ▢ ____________
- ▢ ____________
- ▢ ____________
- ▢ ____________
- ▢ ____________

NOTES

Date: / /

Day 87: Lacking Nothing

If you are lacking anything, ask God. Ask God for help in your shortcomings. Ask God for a baby and for pregnancy, but also ask him for guidance, wisdom, understanding, and direction. God is our provider, who continues to provide according to his Word.

SCRIPTURE

James 1:5, "If any of you lacks wisdom, let him ask God, who gives generously to all without reproach, and it will be given him."

MARK WHERE YOU ARE TODAY

Anxiety 0% ______ 100%

Depression 0% ______ 100%

Peace 0% ______ 100%

Today I am grateful for:

______

______

______

______

Today God has shown me his faithfulness by:

______

______

______

______

What areas of your life are lacking wisdom?

______

______

______

______

What are you lacking today that God can provide?

______

______

______

______

HOW HAS GOD GIVEN GENEROUSLY TO YOU ALREADY?

TODAY'S CHECKLIST

- ▢ Read the Bible
- ▢ Pray
- ▢ Read TTCTF
- ▢ TTCTF Journal
- ▢ ____
- ▢ ____
- ▢ ____
- ▢ ____
- ▢ ____
- ▢ ____
- ▢ ____

NOTES

Date: / /

Day 88: God's Faithfulness

When we lose hope, struggle with patience, and stop putting God first, he remains faithful. The Bible says God is love and the first attribute assigned to love is patience. God will remain faithful to us because he has perfect patience that waits as we figure out how to trust and have faith in him.

SCRIPTURE

Psalm 145:8, "The LORD is gracious and merciful, slow to anger and abounding in steadfast love."

MARK WHERE YOU ARE TODAY

Frustration 0% ____ 100%

Pain 0% ____ 100%

Faith 0% ____ 100%

Today I am grateful for:

Today God has shown me his faithfulness by:

What evidence do you see in your life that shows God's patience?

Why is patience an important attribute of love?

WHAT INSPIRES YOU TO BE FAITHFUL TO GOD?

TODAY'S CHECKLIST

- ▢ Read the Bible
- ▢ Pray
- ▢ Read TTCTF
- ▢ TTCTF Journal
- ▢ ______
- ▢ ______
- ▢ ______
- ▢ ______
- ▢ ______
- ▢ ______
- ▢ ______

NOTES

Date: / /

Day 89: Read the Bible Daily

When we commit to reading the Bible on a daily basis, God speaks to us through his Word. His Word builds confidence in the promises he has given. The Bible is living and active because God speaks to us through it. When we have no direction, we are in the dark. God promises a lamp at our feet through the Word.

SCRIPTURE

Hebrews 4:12, "For the word of God is living and active, sharper than any two-edged sword, piercing to the division of soul and of spirit, of joints and of marrow, and discerning the thoughts and intentions of the heart."

MARK WHERE YOU ARE TODAY

Brokenness 0% ______ 100%

Anger 0% ______ 100%

Joy 0% ______ 100%

Today I am grateful for:

______

______

______

______

Today God has shown me his faithfulness by:

______

______

______

______

What are the downfalls of not reading the Bible?

______

______

______

______

What are the benefits of reading the Bible?

______

______

______

______

WHAT CAN YOU DO TO COMMIT TO READING THE BIBLE EVERY DAY?

TODAY'S CHECKLIST

- ▢ Read the Bible
- ▢ Pray
- ▢ Read TTCTF
- ▢ TTCTF Journal
- ▢ ____________
- ▢ ____________
- ▢ ____________
- ▢ ____________
- ▢ ____________
- ▢ ____________
- ▢ ____________

NOTES

Date: / /

Day 90: God Answers Prayers

God is faithful to his promises in his Word. When we are facing another negative pregnancy test, we cannot lose sight of the fact that God is God. He will answer our prayers according to his Word. No one else can make such a promise. When this gets hard, look to the Word for his promises.

SCRIPTURE

John 15:7, "If you abide in me, and my words abide in you, ask whatever you wish, and it will be done for you."

MARK WHERE YOU ARE TODAY

Wisdom	0%		100%
Discernment	0%		100%
Patience	0%		100%

Today I am grateful for:

____

____

____

____

Today God has shown me his faithfulness by:

____

____

____

____

How do you abide in God?

____

____

____

____

How does God's Word abide in you?

____

____

____

____

HOW DO YOU GET TO THE POINT WHERE YOU CAN ASK GOD WHATEVER YOU WISH AND HE WILL PROVIDE IT?

TODAY'S CHECKLIST

- ▢ Read the Bible
- ▢ Pray
- ▢ Read TTCTF
- ▢ TTCTF Journal
- ▢
- ▢
- ▢
- ▢
- ▢
- ▢
- ▢

NOTES

Date: / /

Day 91: When Darkness Turns to Light

When we wander in darkness, we are guessing which way to go to reach our goals. God provides his light for us when we are facing the unknown of our future. If all God shows us is one step, it is still so much more than walking blindly. We need to keep looking for that light even if we do not see the whole path.

SCRIPTURE

1 John 1:5–7, "...God is light, and in him is no darkness at all. If we say we have fellowship with him while we walk in darkness, we lie and do not practice the truth. But if we walk in the light, as he is in the light, we have fellowship with one another, and the blood of Jesus his Son cleanses us from all sin."

DRAW THE SIZE OF YOUR FAITH

Today I am grateful for:

____

____

____

____

____

Today God has shown me his faithfulness by:

____

____

____

____

What does it mean to "walk in the light"?

____

____

____

How are you walking in darkness?

____

____

____

____

WHAT DO YOU NEED TO DO TO CONTINUE WALKING IN THE LIGHT?

TODAY'S CHECKLIST

- ☐ Read the Bible
- ☐ Pray
- ☐ Read TTCTF
- ☐ TTCTF Journal
- ☐ ______
- ☐ ______
- ☐ ______
- ☐ ______
- ☐ ______
- ☐ ______
- ☐ ______

NOTES

WHAT'S NEXT

Congratulations, 91 days was a huge commitment!

I would like to encourage you by saying if you are not yet pregnant, your TTCTF journey is not over.

You have spent the last 91 days committed to living by faith. You have committed to renewing your hope and eliminating sin. You have done so much work, and it is important to understand that it was all for something. You are building, restoring, and repairing your relationship with God, and he does not want you to give up now just because the program is over.

Now is a great time to review your journal. Week one and week thirteen intentionally have the same polling questions designed for you to view your progress.

Read the questions and read your answers. Do you relate to that person on Day 1, or have you grown? You might even find yourself wanting to do another 91 days to revisit the questions completely.

You may just want to focus on the scriptures and their context in the Bible.

Make sure you join the Through Faith community for a safe place to share your journey and find encouragement.

You have begun a journey that matters, so make this waiting meaningful. God is still working in you and growing you.

What are you still struggling with?

____

____

____

____

How have you grown while TTCTF?

____

____

____

____

Describe your hope:

Describe your faith:

Describe your relationship with God:

What can you commit to doing next while TTCTF?

This may be a vulnerable moment, I understand. The enemy will try to take advantage of any circumstance to cause division between us and God. Thankfully, God will give you strength to continue, and I cannot wait to hear your conception story!

BONUS

BRICK BY BRICK

GOAL

To remember how to honor God with our actions so he is free to bless us according to his Word.

PSALM 77: IN THE DAY OF TROUBLE I SEEK THE LORD

“I cry aloud to God, aloud to God, and he will hear me. In the day of my trouble I seek the Lord; in the night my hand is stretched out without wearying; my soul refuses to be comforted. When I remember God, I moan; when I meditate, my spirit faints. Selah

You hold my eyelids open; I am so troubled that I cannot speak. I consider the days of old, the years long ago. I said, ‘Let me remember my song in the night; let me meditate in my heart.’ Then my spirit made a diligent search: ‘Will the Lord spurn forever, and never again be favorable? Has his steadfast love forever ceased? Are his promises at an end for all time? Has God forgotten to be gracious? Has he in anger shut up his compassion?’ Selah

Then I said, ‘I will appeal to this, to the years of the right hand of the Most High.’

I will remember the deeds of the LORD; yes, I will remember your wonders of old. I will ponder all your work, and meditate on your mighty deeds. Your way, O God, is holy. What god is great like our God? You are the God who works wonders; you have made known your might among the peoples. You with your arm redeemed your people, the children of Jacob and Joseph. Selah

When the waters saw you, O God, when the waters saw you, they were afraid; indeed, the deep trembled. The clouds poured out water; the skies gave forth thunder; your arrows flashed on every side. The crash of your thunder was in the whirlwind; your lightnings lighted up the world; the earth trembled and shook. Your way was through the sea, your path through the great waters; yet your footprints were unseen. You led your people like a flock by the hand of Moses and Aaron.”

Date: / /

Day 1: Recognize We Cannot Do This Without God

We are drastically limited by our abilities. Sometimes it takes recognizing those limitations before we can truly understand how unlimited God is. His reach goes beyond our imagination, and when our will lines up with his will, we can expect to receive all of the promises and blessings God's Word has for us.

SCRIPTURE

Philippians 4:19, "And my God will supply every need of yours according to his riches in glory in Christ Jesus."

FILL IN THE BLANK:

It is important to recognize we cannot do this without ________________.

Today I am grateful for:

____

____

____

____

Today I will build with God by:

____

____

____

____

We started as dust. How does that make you feel about your abilities versus God's?

____

____

____

____

How can you accept God's help as you are TTCTF?

____

____

____

____

WHEN WE GIVE GOD AUTHORITY IN OUR LIVES, WHAT DO WE GET TO ELIMINATE FROM OUR RESPONSIBILITY?

TODAY'S CHECKLIST

- ▢ Read the Bible
- ▢ Pray
- ▢ Read TTCTF
- ▢ TTCTF Journal
- ▢
- ▢
- ▢
- ▢
- ▢
- ▢
- ▢

NOTES

Date: / /

Day 2: Read the Bible and Memorize Relevant Scriptures

It is important to commit to reading and memorizing the Bible. If you wish God would just speak to you and tell you what to do, he does so through the Bible. If you are not reading the Bible, you are missing important instructions God wants you to have. It is amazing how relevant the Bible is to all of our lives no matter what we are facing.

SCRIPTURE

Psalm 119:11, "I have stored up your word in my heart, that I might not sin against you."

FILL IN THE BLANK:

It is important to read the Bible

and ________________

scriptures.

Today I am grateful for:

____

____

____

____

Today I will build with God by:

____

____

____

____

What is your favorite Bible verse?

____

____

____

____

What Bible verse is confusing to you right now?

____

____

____

____

____

WHAT ARE FIVE SCRIPTURES YOU WANT TO WORK ON MEMORIZING?

TODAY'S CHECKLIST

- ▢ Read the Bible
- ▢ Pray
- ▢ Read TTCTF
- ▢ TTCTF Journal
- ▢ ____________
- ▢ ____________
- ▢ ____________
- ▢ ____________
- ▢ ____________
- ▢ ____________
- ▢ ____________

NOTES

Date: / /

Day 3: Seek God Constantly for Answers

When we pray and do not hear from God, it is important to keep searching him for answers. God may want something more from us before providing that answer. If we consistently seek him for answers to our prayers and for guidance, we will get directed to answers. If we do the work, God will show up every time.

SCRIPTURE

2 Chronicles 15:2, "The LORD is with you while you are with him. If you seek him, he will be found by you, but if you forsake him, he will forsake you."

FILL IN THE BLANK:

It is wise to seek ___________ constantly for answers.

Today I am grateful for:

____

____

____

____

____

Today I will build with God by:

____

____

____

____

Why do you think you are not hearing from God?

____

____

____

____

When you face hardships, how do you respond to God?

____

____

____

____

HOW CAN YOU SEEK GOD?

TODAY'S CHECKLIST

- ▢ Read the Bible
- ▢ Pray
- ▢ Read TTCTF
- ▢ TTCTF Journal
- ▢ ______
- ▢ ______
- ▢ ______
- ▢ ______
- ▢ ______
- ▢ ______
- ▢ ______

NOTES

Date: / /

Day 4: Do Not Accept "No" From Anyone Other Than God

The thought of "No" is crushing, especially if we hear it from a professional. Professionals are able to look at science and circumstances and draw conclusions based on their resources, but God's resources go beyond what any professional has access to. When we accept that a few words raised a man from the dead, then we can begin to grasp that what is impossible with man truly is possible with God.

SCRIPTURE

1 Chronicles 29:11, "Yours, O LORD, is the greatness and the power and the glory and the victory and the majesty, for all that is in the heavens and in the earth is yours. Yours is the kingdom, O LORD, and you are exalted as head above all."

FILL IN THE BLANK:

It is important to only listen to ________________ as the authority in my life.

Today I am grateful for:

____

____

____

____

____

Today I will build with God by:

____

____

____

____

____

How can a "no" from someone else give God glory?

____

____

____

Why did God give us limitations?

____

____

____

HOW CAN YOU FIND PEACE AFTER FACING A "NO" FROM SOMEONE OTHER THAN GOD?

TODAY'S CHECKLIST

- ☐ Read the Bible
- ☐ Pray
- ☐ Read TTCTF
- ☐ TTCTF Journal
- ☐
- ☐
- ☐
- ☐
- ☐
- ☐
- ☐

NOTES

Date: / /

Day 5: Be Confident in God's Promises

The enemy has a goal to strip us of all the good things God has planned for us. If we doubt, question, or lose hope in God and the promises he has given us, the enemy wins. When we are unwavering in our faith in God, there will be no place for doubt, questioning, or losing hope.

SCRIPTURE

Hebrews 4:16, "Let us then with confidence draw near to the throne of grace, that we may receive mercy and find grace to help in time of need."

FILL IN THE BLANK:

It is important to be __________ in God's promises.

Today I am grateful for:

____

____

____

____

Today I will build with God by:

____

____

____

____

How can you find God's grace and mercy?

____

____

____

____

How can you be confident in God while TTCTF?

____

____

____

____

____

LIST 5 PROMISES IN THE BIBLE THAT ARE SPECIFICALLY FOR YOU TO RECEIVE:

TODAY'S CHECKLIST

- ☐ Read the Bible
- ☐ Pray
- ☐ Read TTCTF
- ☐ TTCTF Journal
- ☐
- ☐
- ☐
- ☐
- ☐
- ☐
- ☐

NOTES

Date: / /

Day 6: Faith in God No Matter What

Today is the perfect day to get pregnant—from our perspective. But we do not have God's understanding, wisdom, or knowledge. We have to have faith even if our prayers are not answered today, because God is capable. Waiting does not take away from God's abilities or strength. We have to ensure our faith is without doubt, no matter the circumstances.

SCRIPTURE

James 1:6, "But let him ask in faith, with no doubting, for the one who doubts is like a wave of the sea that is driven and tossed by the wind."

FILL IN THE BLANK:

It is crucial to have

________________ in God

no matter what.

Today I am grateful for:

____

____

____

____

Today I will build with God by:

____

____

____

____

How can you be stable in your faith?

____

____

____

____

When does your faith waver?

____

____

____

____

WHY DO YOU THINK YOU ARE NOT PREGNANT YET?

TODAY'S CHECKLIST

- ☐ Read the Bible
- ☐ Pray
- ☐ Read TTCTF
- ☐ TTCTF Journal
- ☐ ____
- ☐ ____
- ☐ ____
- ☐ ____
- ☐ ____
- ☐ ____
- ☐ ____

NOTES

Date: / /

Day 7: Dig Deeper When Obstacles Arise

On the days when everything is a little bit harder and we are facing obstacles through our frustration and disappointment, we cannot lose sight of God. We cannot let our problems distance us further from him. Instead, we need to use this time to run to God even more.

SCRIPTURE

James 1:12, "Blessed is the man who remains steadfast under trial, for when he has stood the test he will receive the crown of life, which God has promised to those who love him."

FILL IN THE BLANK:

I must dig deeper when

_______________________.

Today I am grateful for:

____

____

____

____

____

Today I will build with God by:

____

____

____

____

When days are hard, how can you lean on God to help you get through it?

____

____

____

____

Write two single-sentence prayers you can say when you are struggling with TTCTF:

____

____

____

____

____

LIST 5 OF GOD'S CHARACTERISTICS YOU FIND IN THE BIBLE:

TODAY'S CHECKLIST

- ▢ Read the Bible
- ▢ Pray
- ▢ Read TTCTF
- ▢ TTCTF Journal
- ▢ __________
- ▢ __________
- ▢ __________
- ▢ __________
- ▢ __________
- ▢ __________
- ▢ __________

NOTES

Date: / /

Day 8: "Unrelated" Sin Is All Related to God

God knows us. He knows our thoughts and actions, and it is his desire that we follow and obey his Word. All that we are matters to God. This means we have to deal with all of our sin if we want to honor him with our lives and restore our relationship with him.

SCRIPTURE

Deuteronomy 28:1-2, "And if you faithfully obey the voice of the LORD your God, being careful to do all his commandments that I command you today, the LORD your God will set you high above all the nations of the earth. And all these blessings shall come upon you and overtake you, if you obey the voice of the LORD your God."

FILL IN THE BLANK:

I must ________________ unrelated sin over to God.

Today I am grateful for:

____
____
____
____
____
____

Today I will build with God by:

____
____
____
____
____

Why does God care about every little thing we do?

____
____
____

What sins do you need to work on to honor God?

____
____
____

HOW DO YOUR SINS IMPACT YOUR RELATIONSHIP WITH GOD?

TODAY'S CHECKLIST

- ▢ Read the Bible
- ▢ Pray
- ▢ Read TTCTF
- ▢ TTCTF Journal
- ▢ ____________
- ▢ ____________
- ▢ ____________
- ▢ ____________
- ▢ ____________
- ▢ ____________
- ▢ ____________

NOTES

Date: / /

Day 9: Consistently Grow Closer to God

If we do not make God a priority, our relationship with him will be strained. We know God wants us to put the effort into our relationship. We cannot let our busy lives get in the way of our relationship with God. He has given us all that we have and can help guide and direct us so we are not wasting time living outside of his will.

SCRIPTURE

Matthew 6:33, "But seek first the kingdom of God and his righteousness, and all these things will be added to you."

FILL IN THE BLANK:

I must ________________

grow closer to God.

Today I am grateful for:

____

____

____

____

Today I will build with God by:

____

____

____

____

How are you prioritizing God?

____

____

____

____

What gets in the way of putting God first?

____

____

____

____

____

WHAT DOES A GOOD RELATIONSHIP WITH GOD PRODUCE?

TODAY'S CHECKLIST

- ▢ Read the Bible
- ▢ Pray
- ▢ Read TTCTF
- ▢ TTCTF Journal
- ▢ ____________
- ▢ ____________
- ▢ ____________
- ▢ ____________
- ▢ ____________
- ▢ ____________
- ▢ ____________

NOTES

Day 10: Do Not Minimize God's Power

Whatever mountain we face today pales in comparison to God. He is mighty and powerful, awesome and good. If we lose sight of how big God is, doubt will make us lose faith. Since God answers prayers according to our faith, we will be limiting ourselves from receiving God's blessings.

SCRIPTURE

Ephesians 3:20, "Now to him who is able to do far more abundantly than all that we ask or think, according to the power at work within us..."

FILL IN THE BLANK:

It is important to

_____________ *God's power.*

Today I am grateful for:

____

____

____

____

Today I will build with God by:

____

____

____

____

What are 3 reasons God does not answer prayers right away?

____

____

____

____

What does God think about the desires of your heart?

____

____

____

____

____

WHAT CAN YOU DO TO MAXIMIZE GOD'S POWER WORKING IN YOUR LIFE?

TODAY'S CHECKLIST

- ☐ Read the Bible
- ☐ Pray
- ☐ Read TTCTF
- ☐ TTCTF Journal
- ☐
- ☐
- ☐
- ☐
- ☐
- ☐
- ☐

NOTES

Thank you

Thank you so much for taking the time to follow this journal. I pray to our God in Heaven, who created us, that this journal will be a tool to help you ultimately reach your goal of becoming pregnant.

God is our answer, and his Word is the greatest gift for instruction and direction.

Do not accept no unless God says no!

PRAYERS

This book is full of prayers designed to help guide you as you are TTCTF. I have recorded all of the prayers so you can listen to them daily to help you grow and encourage your walk with God.

Download them for **free** at ttctf.com/resources

CONNECT WITH ME

I would love to hear from you!

Visit my website below to connect with me and to check out the Through Faith community. Here you can also send me an email and join my newsletter to stay connected with me.

I look forward to seeing God work in you during this season and hearing your testimony of a successful pregnancy!

www.ttctf.com/resources

*If this journal has helped you in any way, please consider sharing your experience on Amazon through a review. It means a lot to me and will help encourage other women in the same situation to start TTCTF!

Made in the USA
Monee, IL
29 May 2022